AS Biology
UNIT 1

Specification A

Module 1: Molecules, Cells and Systems

Steve Potter

Philip Allan Updates
Market Place
Deddington
Oxfordshire
OX15 0SE

Tel: 01869 338652
Fax: 01869 337590
e-mail: sales@philipallan.co.uk
www.philipallan.co.uk

ISBN-13: 978-0-86003-486-5
ISBN-10: 0-86003-486-0

This Guide has been written specifically to support students preparing for the AQA Specification A AS Biology Unit 1 examination. The content has been neither approved nor endorsed by AQA and remains the sole responsibility of the author.

Typeset by Magnet Harlequin, Oxford
Printed by MPG Books, Bodmin

Contents

Introduction

About this guide 4

Preparing for the Unit 1 test 5

Approaching the unit test 6

■ ■ ■

Content Guidance

About this section 10

Microscopy and cell structure 11

Plasma membranes and the passage of molecules 15

Molecules in biological systems.. 19

The nature and action of enzymes 27

Tissues organs and systems.. 34

The circulatory and breathing systems at rest and during exercise........................ 38

■ ■ ■

Questions and Answers

About this section.. 54

Q1 The breathing system and diffusion 55

Q2 Cell structure... 58

Q3 Tissues, organs and the circulatory system................................... 60

Q4 Molecules in biological systems (I) 62

Q5 Blood and the passage of substances... 64

Q6 The nature and action of enzymes 66

Q7 Microscopy and cell structure 70

Q8 Molecules in biological systems (II) 73

Q9 Plasma membranes.. 76

Q10 The circulatory system 81

Introduction

About this guide

This guide is written to help you to prepare for the Unit 1 examination of the AQA Biology Specification A. Unit 1 examines the content of **Module 1: Molecules, Cells and Systems**, and forms part of the AS assessment. It will also form part of the A2 assessment with some of the material being re-examined in the end of A2 synoptic examination.

This Introduction provides guidance on revision, together with advice on approaching the examination itself.

The Content Guidance section gives a point-by-point description of all the facts you need to know and concepts you need to understand for Module 1. Although each fact and concept is explained where necessary, you must be prepared to use other resources in your preparation.

The Question and Answer section shows you the sort of questions you can expect in the unit test. It would be impossible to give examples of every kind of question in one book, but these should give you a flavour of what to expect. Each question has been attempted by two candidates, Candidate A and Candidate B. Their answers, along with the examiner's comments, should help you to see what you need to do to score a good mark — and how you can easily *not* score a mark even though you probably understand the biology.

What can I assume about the guide?

You can assume that:
- the topics described in the Content Guidance section correspond to those in the specification
- the basic facts you need to know are stated clearly
- the major concepts you need to understand are explained
- the questions at the end of the guide are similar in style to those that will appear in the unit test
- the answers supplied are genuine answers — not concocted by the author
- the standard of the marking is broadly equivalent to the standard that will be applied to your answers

What can I *not* assume about the guide?

You *must not* assume that:
- every last detail has been covered
- the diagrams used will be the same as those used in a unit test (they may be more or less detailed, seen from a different angle etc.)

- the way in which the concepts are explained is the *only* way in which they can be presented in an examination (often concepts are presented in an unfamiliar situation)
- the range of question types presented is exhaustive (examiners are always thinking of new ways to test a topic)

So how should I use this guide?

The guide lends itself to a number of uses throughout your course — it is not *just* a revision aid. Because the Content Guidance is laid out in sections that correspond to those of the specification for Module 1, you can:
- use it to check that your notes cover the material required by the specification
- use it to identify strengths and weaknesses
- use it as a reference for homework and internal tests
- use it during your revision to prepare 'bite-sized' chunks of related material, rather than being faced with a file full of notes

The Question and Answer section can be used to:
- identify the terms used by examiners in questions and what they expect of you
- familiarise yourself with the style of questions you can expect
- identify the ways in which marks are lost as well as the ways in which they are gained

Preparing for the Unit 1 test

Preparation for examinations is a very personal thing. Different people prepare, equally successfully, in very different ways. The key is being totally honest about what actually *works* for *you*. This is *not* necessarily the same as the style you would like to adopt. It is no use preparing to a background of rock music if this distracts you.

Whatever your style, you must have a plan. Sitting down the night before the examination with a file full of notes and a textbook does not constitute a revision plan — it is just desperation — and you must not expect a great deal from it. Whatever your personal style, there are a number of things you *must* do and a number of other things you *could* do.

Things you *must* do

- Leave yourself enough time to cover *all* the material.
- Make sure that you actually *have* all the material to hand (use this book as a basis).
- Identify weaknesses early in your preparation so that you have time to do something about them.
- Familiarise yourself with the terminology used in examination questions (see p. 6).

Things you *could* do to help you learn

- Copy selected portions of your notes.
- Write a precis of your notes which includes all the key points.

- Write key points on postcards (carry them round with you for a quick revise during a coffee break!).
- Discuss a topic with a friend also studying the same course.
- Try to explain a topic to someone *not* on the course.
- Practise examination questions on the topic.

Approaching the unit test

Terms used in examination questions

You will be asked precise questions in the examinations so you can save a lot of valuable time as well as ensuring you score as many marks as possible by knowing what is expected. Terms most commonly used are explained below.

Describe

This means exactly what it says — 'tell me about...' — and you should not need to explain why.

Explain

Here you must give biological reasons for *why* or *how* something is happening.

Complete

You must finish off a diagram, graph, flow chart or table.

Draw/plot

This means that you must construct some type of graph. For this, make sure that:
- you choose a scale that makes good use of the graph paper (if a scale is not given) and does not leave all the plots tucked away in one corner
- plot an appropriate type of graph — if both variables are continuous variables, then a line graph is usually the most appropriate; if one is a discrete variable, then a bar chart is appropriate
- plot carefully using a sharp pencil and draw lines accurately

From the...

This means that you must use only information in the diagram/graph/photograph or other forms of data.

Name

This asks you to give the name of a structure/molecule/organism etc.

Suggest

This means 'give a plausible biological explanation for' — it is often used when testing understanding of concepts in an unfamiliar situation.

Compare

In this case you have to give similarities *and* differences between...

Calculate

This means add, subtract, multiply, divide (do some kind of sum!) and show how you got your answer — *always show your working!*

When you finally open the test paper, it can be quite a stressful moment. You may not recognise the diagram or graph used in question 1. It can be quite demoralising to attempt a question at the start of an examination if you are not feeling very confident about it. So:

- *do not* begin to write as soon as you open the paper
- *do not* answer question 1 first, just because it is printed first (the examiner did not sequence the questions with your particular favourites in mind)
- *do* scan *all* the questions before you begin to answer any
- *do* identify those questions about which you feel most confident
- *do answer first* those questions about which you feel most confident regardless of order in the paper
- *do read the question carefully* — if you are asked to explain, then explain, don't just describe
- *do* take notice of the mark allocation and don't supply the examiner with all your knowledge of osmosis if there is only 1 mark allocated (similarly, you will have to come up with four ideas if 4 marks are allocated)
- *do* try to stick to the point in your answer (it is easy to stray into related areas that will not score marks and will use up valuable time)
- *do* take care with
    - drawings — you will not be asked to produce complex diagrams, but those you do produce must resemble the subject
    - labelling — label lines *must touch* the part you are required to identify; if they stop short or pass through the part, you will lose marks
    - graphs — draw *small* points if you are asked to plot a graph and join the plots with ruled lines or, if specifically asked for, a line or smooth curve of best fit through all the plots
- *do try* to answer *all* the questions

Content Guidance

This section is a guide to the content of **Module 1: Molecules, Cells and Systems**. The main areas of this module are:

- Microscopy and cell structure
- Plasma membranes and the passage of substances into and out of cells
- Molecules in biological systems
- The nature and action of enzymes
- Tissues, organs and systems
- The circulatory and breathing systems at rest and during exercise

You should think of this section as a 'translation' of the specification from 'examiner speak' into more user-friendly language. At the same time I have tried to be very precise in describing exactly what is required of you. This is done for each area in the module under the headings described below.

Key facts you must know

These are exactly what you might think: a summary of all the basic knowledge that you must be able to recall. All the actual knowledge has been broken down into a number of small facts that you must learn. This means that the list of 'Key facts' for some topics is quite long. However, this approach makes quite clear *everything* you need to know about the topic. You need to learn the key facts for a topic before you try to understand the key concepts.

Key concepts you must understand

These are a little different: whereas you can learn facts, you must *understand* these ideas or concepts. You can know the actual words that describe a concept like osmosis, or resolving power of a microscope, but you will not be able to use this information unless you really understand what is going on. Once you genuinely understand a concept, you will probably not have to learn it again. I have given brief explanations of all the major concepts, but you must be prepared to refer to your notes and textbooks or ask your teacher for a fuller explanation.

What the examiners will expect you to be able to do

In this part, I have tried to give you an insight into the minds of the examiners who will set and mark your examination papers. Obviously, they may ask you to recall any of the basic knowledge or explain any of the key concepts; but they may well do more than that. Examiners think up questions where the concepts you understand are in a different setting or context from the one(s) you are familiar with. I have tried, in this section, to prepare you for the sorts of questions they might ask. This can never be exhaustive, but it will give you a good idea of what can be asked of you. Bear in mind that examiners will often set individual questions that involve knowledge and understanding of more than one section. The sample questions in the Question and Answer section of this book will help you to practise this skill.

After each topic there is a short paragraph marked 'Links'. While not crucial to the understanding of any of the biology, this should give you some idea of how the biology you are learning will be related to other topics that you may meet in other modules.

Microscopy and cell structure

Microscopy

To understand the structure of cells you must be able to look at detailed images of them. These are provided by light microscopes and electron microscopes. You must understand what you are seeing when you look through a light microscope and when you look at the micrographs formed by transmission electron microscopes and scanning electron microscopes.

Key facts you must know

You will need to know how images are formed by a light microscope, a transmission electron microscope and a scanning electron microscope. The diagrams on page 12 summarise this.

In the light microscope and the transmission electron microscope the images are formed from the light rays or electrons that pass through the specimen. Areas where more light or more electrons pass through appear brighter. In the scanning electron microscope, the images are formed from the electrons that bounce off the specimen. Areas where more electrons bounce off the specimen appear brighter. The scanning electron microscope produces three-dimensional images.

Feature	Light microscope	Transmission electron microscope	Scanning electron microscope
Illumination	Light	Electrons	Electrons
Resolution	0.2 μm	0.001 μm	0.01 μm
Specimens	Living or dead whole cells, may be stained	Dead sections of cells, dried and stained	Dead, can be whole structures, dried and may be stained
Images	Natural appearance of cells, large organelles visible	May include artefacts due to preparation, all organelles visible	3-D image of whole structure or organism

You will need to be able to stain and mount material (such as onion epidermis) in a temporary slide for use with a light microscope, and know how material is prepared for use in a transmission electron microscope and how this may affect the specimen. Dehydration and the use of heavy metal salts may introduce artefacts.

Key concepts you must understand

You will need to understand the magnification and resolving power of a microscope and how the resolving power depends on the wavelength of the light/electrons.

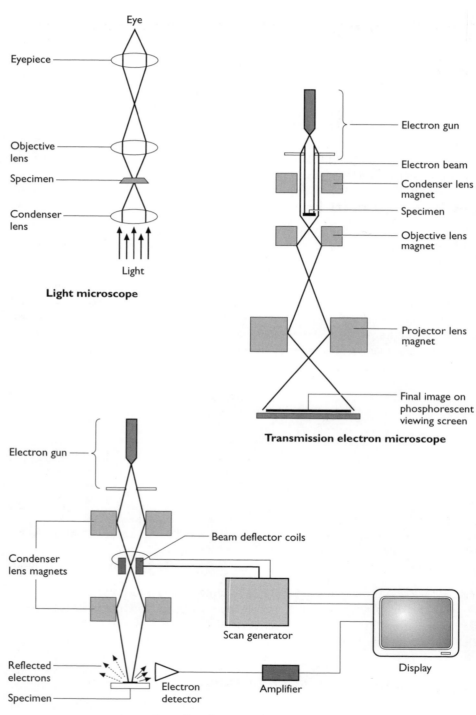

Light microscope

Eye

Eyepiece

Objective lens

Specimen

Condenser lens

Light

Transmission electron microscope

Electron gun

Electron beam

Condenser lens magnet

Specimen

Objective lens magnet

Projector lens magnet

Final image on phosphorescent viewing screen

Scanning electron microscope

Electron gun

Condenser lens magnets

Beam deflector coils

Scan generator

Reflected electrons

Specimen

Electron detector

Amplifier

Display

What the examiners will expect you to be able to do

- Recall any of the key facts.
- Explain any of the key concepts.
- Identify organelles (parts of cells) in a photograph or drawing of a cell as seen through a light microscope (usually cell wall, vacuole, chloroplasts [plant cells only], nucleus, cytoplasm and plasma membrane).
- Identify organelles in a photograph or drawing of a cell as seen through an electron microscope (cell wall, plasma membrane, vacuole, chloroplasts, mitochondria, lysosomes, rough endoplasmic reticulum, smooth endoplasmic reticulum, Golgi apparatus, ribosomes, microvilli and vesicles).
- Calculate either the actual size of an organelle or the magnification from information given or measured by yourself. (Remember that magnification = observed size/actual size, actual size = observed size/magnification and that, as part of your calculation, you may have to convert units — e.g. from mm to μm.)

Tip Remember how big cells actually are! The diameter of most eukaryotic cells is 10–100 μm; that of prokaryotic cells is generally less than 10 μm. If any answer you obtain in an examination differs wildly from this, check your working. Every year I mark the scripts of candidates who don't bother to check and, as a result, they obtain some very strange answers for the size of a cell. These range from 60 000 000 μm (equivalent to two blue whales end-to-end) down to 0.0006 μm (the size of an atom).

Cell structure

The cell is the basic unit of living things, so an understanding of cell structure and function is crucial to many areas of biology. You must understand the basic structure of cells so that you can appreciate how some cells have adapted this structure to perform specific functions. This section gives an overview of cell structure; other sections and other units go into more detail concerning specific organelles.

Key facts you must know

There are two types of cell: prokaryotic cells (including bacterial cells) and eukaryotic cells (including plant and animal cells). Prokaryotic cells are smaller and contain fewer organelles than eukaryotic cells. Those that they do contain are not bound by membranes.

The functions, in outline, of the organelles are as follows:
- the **nucleus** contains DNA which controls protein synthesis through mRNA
- **ribosomes** synthesise proteins
- **mitochondria** are the sites where many of the reactions of aerobic respiration take place and where ATP is formed
- **chloroplasts** are the sites of photosynthesis

- **lysosomes** contain a mixture of hydrolytic enzymes — they are used to digest old or worn out organelles in the cell, to digest bacteria once engulfed by white blood cells and to get rid of surplus tissue, such as extra muscle formed in the uterus during pregnancy
- **rough endoplasmic reticulum (rough ER)** is an internal membrane system with ribosomes attached to it — proteins made in the ribosomes accumulate in the rough ER and are passed to the Golgi apparatus
- **smooth endoplasmic reticulum (smooth ER)** is an internal membrane system without ribosomes attached — it produces steroids
- the **Golgi apparatus** modifies proteins (for example by adding carbohydrate to them to make glycoproteins) that are synthesised in the ribosomes and transported by the rough ER; it releases **vesicles** (sacs) containing the modified proteins which fuse with the plasma membrane to secrete the protein (this is called **exocytosis**)
- the **plasma membrane** controls what enters and leaves the cell (the next section deals with this in detail) but it has *virtually no physical strength*
- **microvilli** are finger-like foldings of the plasma membrane that increase the surface area available for absorption of molecules
- the **cell wall**, where present (e.g. bacteria and plants), provides rigidity and support for the cell; plant cell walls are made from cellulose fibrils

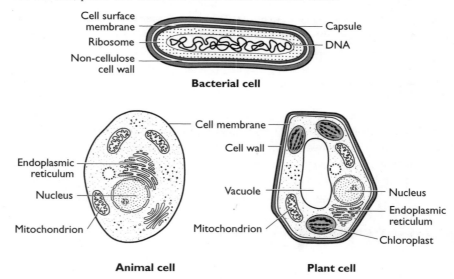

Bacterial cell

Animal cell　　　　**Plant cell**

Key concepts you must understand

Cell fractionation separates the different organelles on the basis of their mass by spinning them in an ultra-centrifuge at varying speeds. Heavier organelles, such as the nucleus, are spun down at low speeds; the lighter ribosomes only spin down at much higher speeds. Tissue is prepared for ultra-centrifugation by homogenising in a blender in an ice-cold (to reduce enzyme damage), isotonic (to prevent osmotic damage) buffer (to stabilise pH) solution.

Tip Be clear in your mind that the solution needs to be isotonic to prevent osmotic damage to the *organelles* and not to the cells — these will be quite seriously damaged when they are burst open by homogenising them in the blender!

What the examiners will expect you to be able to do

- Recall any of the key facts.
- Explain any of the key concepts.
- Distinguish between prokaryotic and eukaryotic cells, giving reasons (DNA in prokaryotic cells is 'naked' — not bound to histone proteins, DNA is not contained within a nucleus, there are no organelles such as mitochondria and chloroplasts, there are no internal membranes and the ribosomes are smaller than those in eukaryotic cells).
- Relate the speed of centrifuging during cell fractionation to the organelles spun down.
- Label structures shown on drawings of bacterial cells (cell wall, capsule and DNA).
- Label structures shown on drawings of plant and animal cells.
- Relate the internal structure of a cell to its function.

Tip A cell with many mitochondria must be very active to need a lot of energy-releasing organelles. A cell with a plasma membrane folded into microvilli must be absorbing a lot of material to need that increased surface area. A cell with both indicates a lot of absorption (microvilli) by active transport (many mitochondria). A cell with an extensive rough ER must be synthesising a lot of proteins.

Links Cells are the basic units of living organisms and all eukaryotic cells share many features. Certain features are modified in specialised cells (e.g. nerve cells and epithelial cells in the small intestine) to make the cell more efficient in performing a particular function. An understanding of the structure of the organelles is fundamental to understanding many biological processes (such as photosynthesis, respiration and protein synthesis). You must understand cell structure to understand cell division and inheritance.

Plasma membranes and the passage of substances

Plasma membranes control what enters and leaves the cell and are important in cell recognition. This section looks at the structure of plasma membranes and how this structure enables them to perform their functions.

Tip Remember — plasma membranes have virtually no physical strength and so give very little support to the cell. Cell walls, where they are present, provide this support.

Key facts you must know

Plasma membranes are made largely from proteins, phospholipids and carbohydrates. The phospholipids are arranged in a bi-layer with phosphate 'heads' pointing outwards and fatty acid 'tails' pointing inwards. The current model of plasma membrane structure is called the fluid mosaic model.

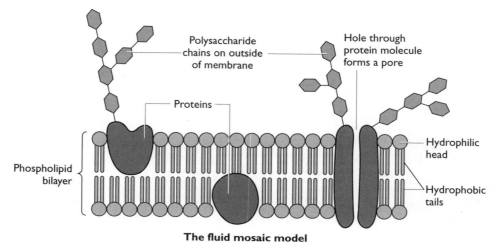

Polysaccharide chains on outside of membrane

Hole through protein molecule forms a pore

Proteins

Hydrophilic head

Phospholipid bilayer

Hydrophobic tails

The fluid mosaic model

The proteins in the membrane serve different functions:
- **hydrophilic/ionic pores** — some proteins form pores which allow water-soluble molecules/ions to pass through the membrane
- **carrier/transport proteins** transport specific molecules through the membrane, some by facilitated diffusion (down the concentration gradient) and others by active transport (against the concentration gradient) using ATP from respiration as the energy source
- **glycoproteins** have a polysaccharide chain that extends outwards from the protein, which is important in cell recognition
- **receptor proteins** act as binding sites for hormones

Small particles are moved across plasma membranes by diffusion, facilitated diffusion, osmosis or active transport. Large particles can be moved across plasma membranes by **endocytosis** (moving *into* the cell) and **exocytosis** (moving *out* of the cell).

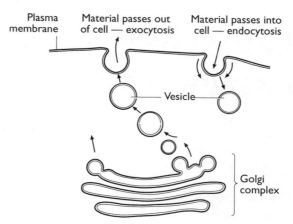

Plasma membrane

Material passes out of cell — exocytosis

Material passes into cell — endocytosis

Vesicle

Golgi complex

Key concepts you must understand

Polar regions of a molecule are those that carry a slight ionic charge and this makes them **hydrophilic** — attracted to water. Non-polar regions of a molecule do not carry any charge and are repelled by water — they are **hydrophobic**. Phospholipids arrange themselves into a bi-layer because of the dual nature of the molecule: polar 'heads' face outwards towards the watery cytoplasm; non-polar 'tails' face inwards away from the watery cytoplasm.

Diffusion is the process by which particles pass from a high concentration to a lower concentration. Diffusion may occur freely in a liquid or gas or may occur across an exchange surface such as a plasma membrane or the walls of the alveoli. The rate of diffusion across an exchange surface is affected by the surface area and thickness of the exchange surface and the difference in concentration on the two sides of the exchange surface. **Fick's law** relates the factors affecting diffusion across an exchange surface in an equation. The rate of diffusion is proportional to:

$$\frac{\text{surface area} \times \text{difference in concentration}}{\text{thickness of exchange surface}}$$

Tip We often talk about particles moving from a high concentration to a lower concentration as moving *down a concentration gradient*. Moving from a low concentration to a higher one is moving *against a concentration gradient*. Use these phrases, but do *not* write about 'moving *along* a concentration gradient' as this is ambiguous — it could mean up or down the gradients and will not gain a mark in an examination.

Non-polar molecules (like lipids) can pass easily through cell membranes because they are not repelled by the lipid part of the membrane. **Polar** (charged/ionic) particles cannot pass through the lipid portions of the membrane as they are repelled: they must pass though special pores or be carried through by transport proteins.

Water potential (ψ) is a measure of the energy water molecules possess which is free to make them move: it is affected by any solutes dissolved in the water (the solute potential or ψ_s) and any physical pressure (the pressure potential or ψ_p) acting on the liquid — such as a plant cell wall 'pressing' on the cytoplasm. Water potential is measured in kiloPascals (kPa).

Tip Pure water has a water potential of zero: this is the highest possible water potential. When a solute is dissolved in water, some of the water molecules form a shell around the solute particles and some of the energy of the water is bound up in this shell. There is less energy left for movement and the water potential is decreased. It is now lower than zero, so must be *negative*. All solutions have a negative water potential. More concentrated solutions have a more negative water potential than less concentrated solutions.

Water moves from an area of high water potential to an area of lower water potential through a partially permeable membrane. This movement is called **osmosis**.

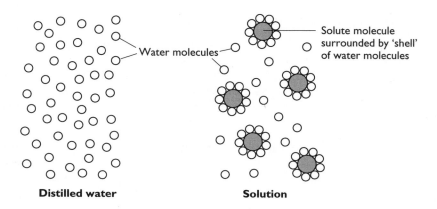

A less negative water potential is a *higher* water potential (nearer to zero) than a *more* negative one, so we can also say that water moves from a solution with a less negative water potential to one with a more negative water potential.

Tip Make a real effort to write about osmosis in terms of water potential. Once you start to describe osmosis in terms of concentrations, the examiner marking your paper will ask 'concentration of what? The solute? The water?' You may lose the marks for not making it sufficiently clear. Water potential is unambiguous.

Osmosis and diffusion are **passive** processes needing only the kinetic energy of the particles themselves (they need no energy (ATP) from respiration).

Tip Be careful when you are describing diffusion and osmosis — it is wrong to say that they need no energy. They *do*. If the particles had no **kinetic** energy they would be stationary!

Active transport moves particles against a concentration gradient and requires energy (ATP) from respiration to do so.

What the examiners will expect you to be able to do

- Recall any of the key facts.
- Explain any of the key concepts.
- Explain why plasma membranes appear as two dark lines separated by a paler region in electron micrographs.
- Explain why increasing the temperature of cells causes the plasma membranes to become 'leaky' — slowly at first and then more rapidly. When the temperature increases, the molecules in the plasma membrane start to move about more (they have more kinetic energy) and this creates 'temporary gaps' in the membrane. Above a critical temperature, the proteins denature and the membrane structure is permanently altered.
- Deduce, from information given, the direction of movement of water in a group of cells with differing water potentials. The diagram shows the direction of water movement in a group of three cells.

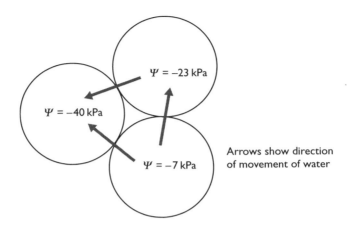

$\Psi = -23$ kPa

$\Psi = -40$ kPa

$\Psi = -7$ kPa

Arrows show direction
of movement of water

Tip Remember, water always moves from a less negative ψ to a more negative ψ.

- Deduce, from concentrations given, whether a substance can move across a membrane by diffusion or active transport.
- Deduce what will happen to an active transport process if the cells involved are fed a respiratory poison (a chemical that stops the process of respiration and, therefore, the release of energy and formation of ATP).
- Explain how the fluid mosaic model of membrane structure allows some cells to change shape.

Links The processes of osmosis, diffusion, facilitated diffusion, active transport, endocytosis and exocytosis are vital to an understanding of how many exchange processes occur. These include gas exchange in the lungs, reabsorption of glucose in kidney tubules, uptake of water by plant roots and many other examples. You will need to understand the basic processes in this module, but you will also need to apply this understanding in other situations in other modules.

Molecules in biological systems

This section looks at the structure and function of some of the important types of biological molecule — carbohydrates, proteins and lipids. Many large biological molecules are polymers of smaller ones joined by condensation reactions. They can be broken down into their monomers (the small molecules) by the process of hydrolysis. The structure of biological molecules is closely related to the functions they perform. Biochemical tests can identify certain molecules and a mixture of molecules can sometimes be separated by using one-way or two-way chromatography. The R_f values obtained from chromatography can be used to identify molecules (see p. 26).

Structure of molecules

Key facts you must know

Carbohydrate molecules contain carbon, hydrogen and oxygen atoms and contain twice as many hydrogen atoms as oxygen atoms.

The atoms in **monosaccharide** carbohydrate molecules can be arranged into a single 'ring'. Glucose is a monosaccharide carbohydrate with the formula $C_6H_{12}O_6$. There are two forms of glucose — alpha- (α-) glucose and beta- (β-) glucose: they contain exactly the same number and types of atoms but the atoms are arranged differently.

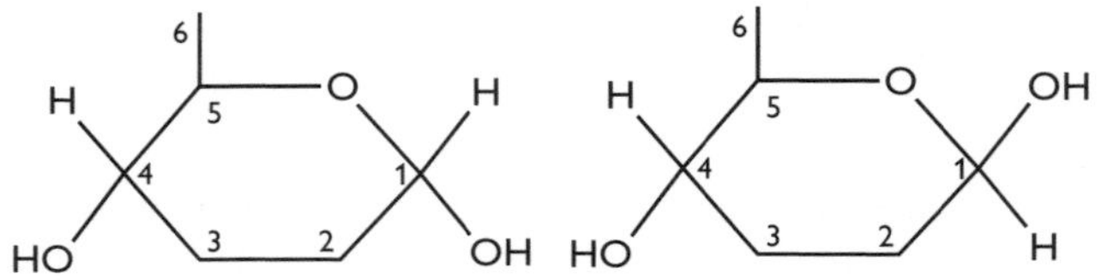

α-Glucose   β-Glucose

The numbers in the diagrams show the positions of the carbon atoms.

Tip You will not need to know where every single atom is in molecules of α- and β-glucose. However, you *will* need to be able to reproduce or interpret these diagrams which show the main features of the molecules.

Disaccharide carbohydrates are formed from two monosaccharides joined by a glycosidic bond. Maltose is a disaccharide carbohydrate in which two molecules of α-glucose are joined by an α (1,4) glycosidic bond. It has the formula $C_{12}H_{22}O_{11}$. The bond is so-called because two molecules of α-glucose are joined. The bond is between carbon atom **1** of one molecule and carbon atom **4** of the other.

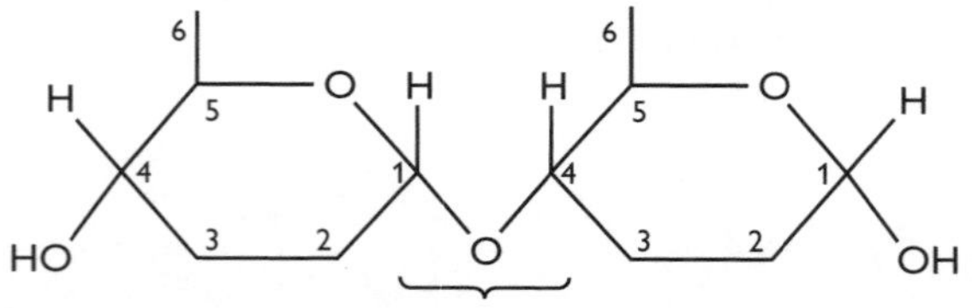

Maltose

Glycosidic bond

Sucrose is a disaccharide carbohydrate in which a molecule of a glucose is joined to a molecule of fructose by a glycosidic bond. It has the formula $C_{12}H_{22}O_{11}$.

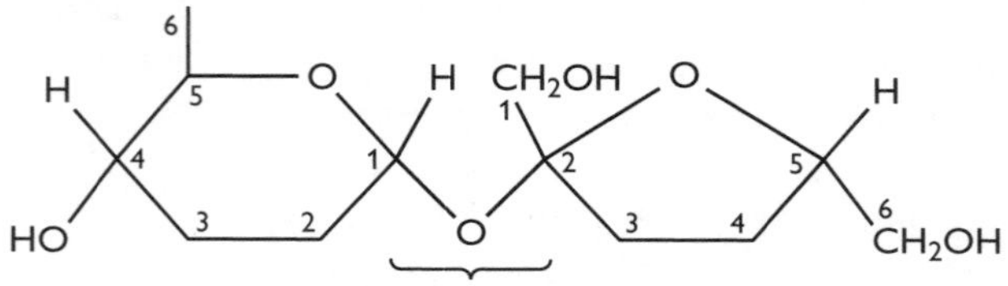

Sucrose

Glycosidic bond

Polysaccharide carbohydrate molecules are formed from many monosaccharides joined by glycosidic bonds. Starch, cellulose and glycogen are polysaccharides: each contains many hundreds of glucose molecules joined by glycosidic bonds to form a long chain.

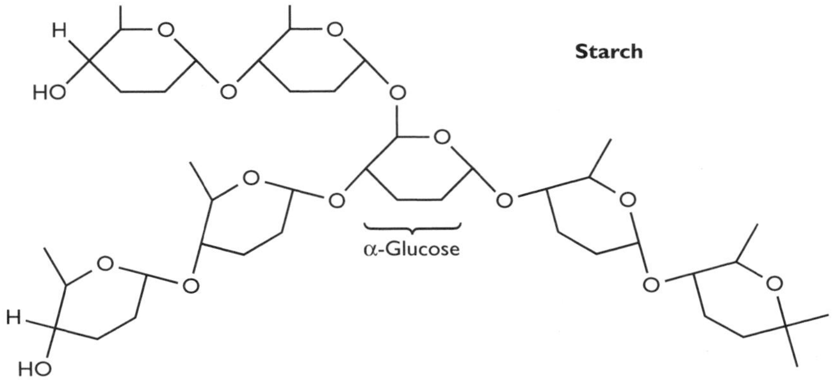

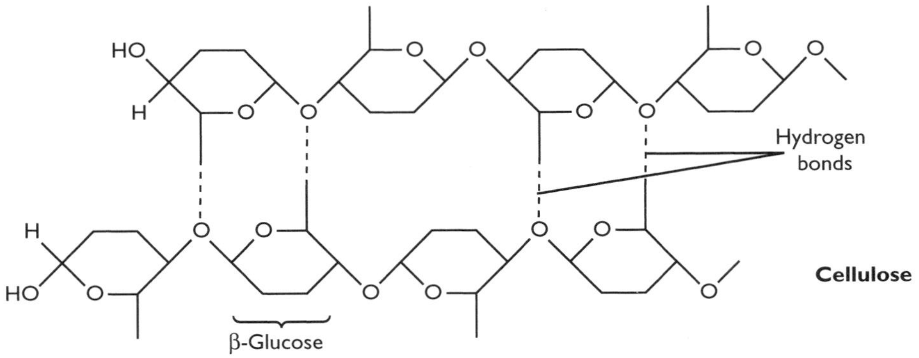

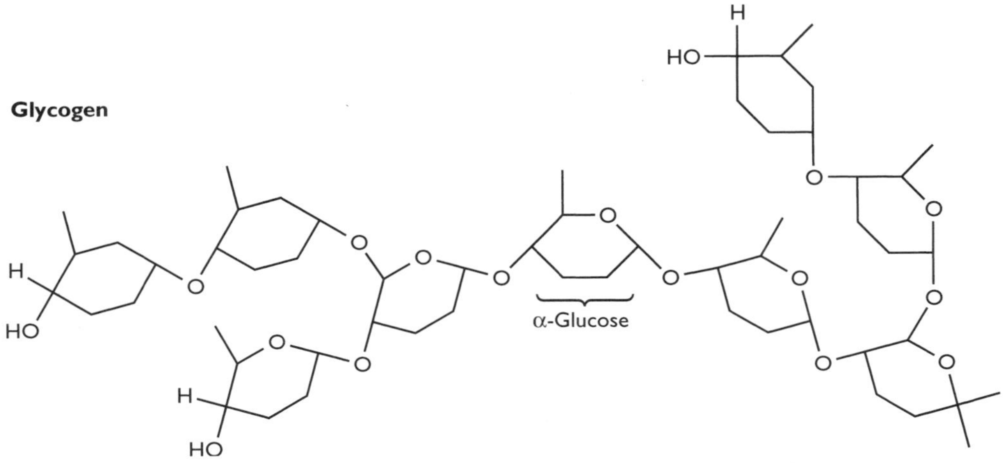

Starch

α-Glucose

Hydrogen bonds

Cellulose

β-Glucose

Glycogen

α-Glucose

Feature	Polysaccharide		
	Starch	Cellulose	Glycogen
Monosaccharide unit	α-Glucose	β-Glucose	α-Glucose
Type of bond	α-Glycosidic	β-Glycosidic	α-Glycosidic
Branches in chain	Few branches	No branches	Many branches
Function	Storage carbohydrate in plants	Structural carbohydrate used in plant cell walls	Storage carbohydrate in animals

Proteins are made from **amino acids**. Amino acids contain atoms of carbon, hydrogen, oxygen and nitrogen. A few also contain sulphur atoms.

Tip The general formula of an amino acid is shown in the diagram. In 'biochemspeak', R stands for radical, but I find it helpful to think of R as 'Rest of molecule'.

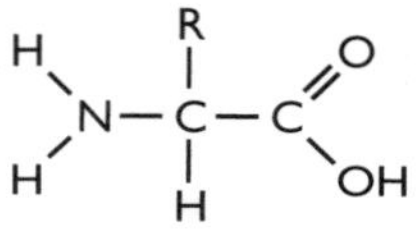

Two amino acids can be joined by peptide bonds to form a **dipeptide**. Many amino acids joined together form a **polypeptide**.

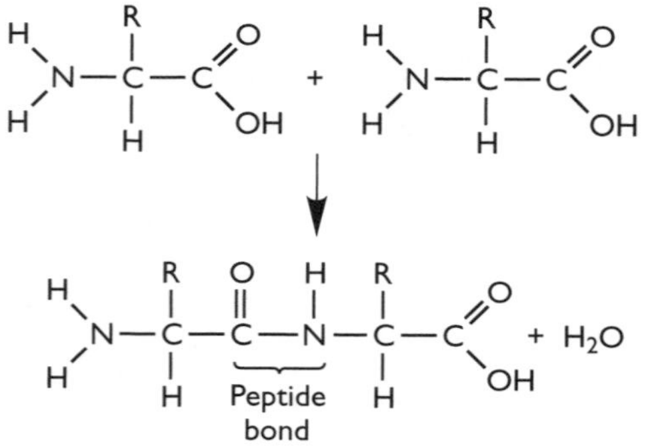

Two amino acids

One dipeptide

The sequence of amino acids in a polypeptide chain is called the **primary structure** of the protein. This polypeptide chain may then be coiled into a helix (called an **α-helix**): this is the **secondary structure** of the protein. The helix may be folded or 'scrunched' into a ball: the **tertiary structure** of the protein.

Tip Think of the cord attaching a telephone handset to the machine itself. The actual cord represents the primary structure; it is then coiled into a helix which is like the secondary structure of a protein. Mine always seems to defy every law of physics to tangle itself into a 'blob' every time I leave it — this is like the tertiary structure of a protein.

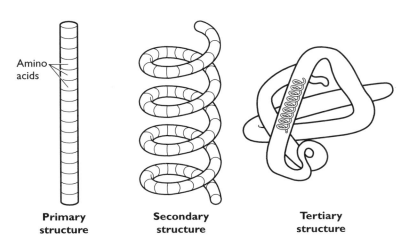

Primary structure   **Secondary structure**   **Tertiary structure**

Proteins with a 'ball'-shaped tertiary structure are called globular proteins. If several tertiary structures are stuck together to make one huge molecule, this overall structure is the **quaternary structure** of the protein.

Lipid molecules contain atoms of carbon, hydrogen and oxygen, but contain much less oxygen than molecules of carbohydrates. **Triglycerides** are a type of lipid in which a glycerol molecule is joined to three fatty acid molecules by ester bonds. **Phospholipids** are lipids in which a glycerol molecule is joined to two fatty acids and one phosphate group.

A triglyceride   **A phospholipid**

Key concepts you must understand

In **condensation reactions** two hydrogen atoms and an oxygen atom are removed from the reacting molecules to create 'spare bonds' which then join to link these molecules into one.

In **hydrolysis reactions**, water is used to break the links formed in condensation reactions.

Glycosidic bonds, peptide bonds and ester bonds are formed by **condensation reactions** and can be broken again by **hydrolysis**. The diagrams below show how.

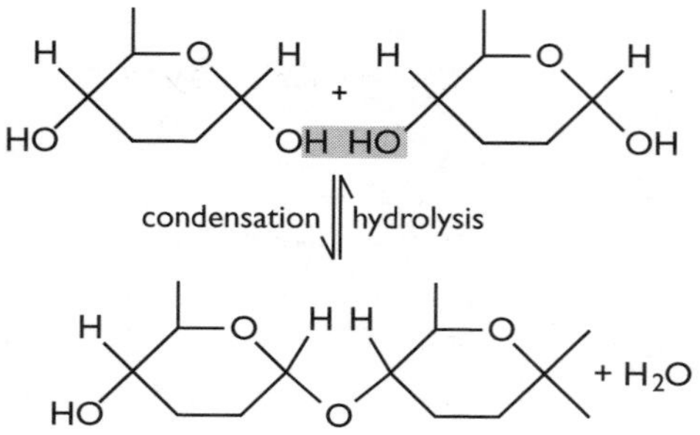

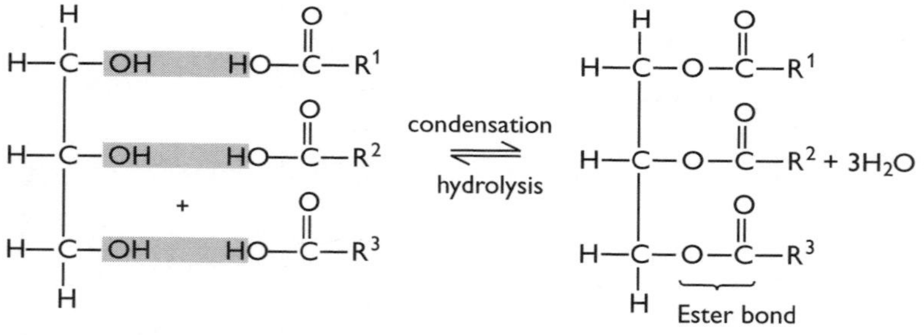

condensation ‖ hydrolysis

$+ H_2O$

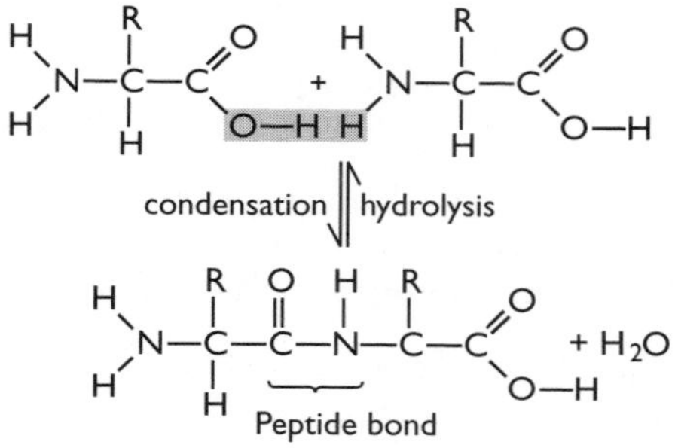

condensation ‖ hydrolysis

Peptide bond

$+ H_2O$

condensation
hydrolysis

Ester bond

$+ 3H_2O$

Starch and glycogen have large molecules which are insoluble in water. This makes them ideal as storage carbohydrates as they have no osmotic effects.

Cellulose molecules are long chains. Many of these are held side-by-side by hydrogen bonds to form fibrils. Many fibrils join to form fibres which can be 'woven' together in plant cell walls to give a strong yet elastic structure.

The primary structure of a protein (the amino acid sequence) determines the secondary structure and the tertiary structure.

The secondary structure is held in place by hydrogen bonds between every fourth amino acid. Hydrogen bonds, ionic bonds and sulphur bridges then form between certain amino acids in the helix to fold it into its tertiary structure.

The tertiary structure of a protein is unique to that protein and this shape allows it to perform a specific function. The following table gives some examples of this.

Example of protein molecule	Effect of specific shape	Consequence
Enzyme	Active site only accepts certain molecules	Enzyme is specific — it will only catalyse one reaction
Insulin receptor in plasma membrane	Insulin only binds with cells with this receptor	Insulin only targets certain cells (e.g. liver cells)
Receptor in 'sweet' taste bud in tongue	Only accepts molecules shaped to fit	These molecules taste sweet

The tertiary structure of a protein is altered by heat. Increasing the temperature causes the atoms in the structure to vibrate more and eventually the bonds that hold the tertiary structure in place are broken — the protein has been **denatured**. Making the pH too acidic or too alkaline can also break bonds in a protein and denature it.

Identifying molecules

Key facts you must know

The **Benedict's test** detects **reducing sugars** such as glucose, fructose, maltose and lactose. In the Benedict's test, the test substance is heated with Benedict's solution for a few minutes: an **orange-red precipitate** shows the presence of a reducing sugar.

Tip Don't forget, it *only works if it is heated.* You will lose marks if you don't mention this in an examination.

The Benedict's test can also be used to test for **non-reducing sugars** such as sucrose — but there are more steps in the test and it must first be shown that there are no reducing sugars present. The table below summarises these tests.

Step in test	Reducing sugar	Non-reducing sugar
Heat with Benedict's solution	Red precipitate	No change — solution remains blue
Conclusion	Reducing sugar present — no further steps	Reducing sugar absent — proceed
Boil with hydrochloric acid for 5 minutes		(Acid hydrolyses non-reducing sugar molecules)
Neutralise with sodium carbonate solution		(Benedict's test won't work in acid solutions)
Re-test with Benedict's solution		Red precipitate
Conclusion		Reducing sugar now present, therefore non-reducing sugar present originally

Starch is detected by the **iodine test**. The test substance is mixed with iodine solution and a **blue-black coloration** shows that starch is present.

The **Biuret test** is used to test for **proteins**. The test substance is mixed with Biuret solution (blue) and left to stand for a few minutes. A **mauve/purple colour** shows that a protein is present. Biuret solution is supplied as a single solution. Alternatively, dilute copper sulphate and sodium hydroxide can be used separately. Both methods give the same result and either will be marked correct in an examination.

The **emulsion test** shows the presence of **lipids**: the test substance is shaken with ethanol (alcohol), filtered and the liquid poured into water — a **milky/white colour** shows that a lipid is present.

Chromatography can sometimes be used to separate a mixture of molecules.

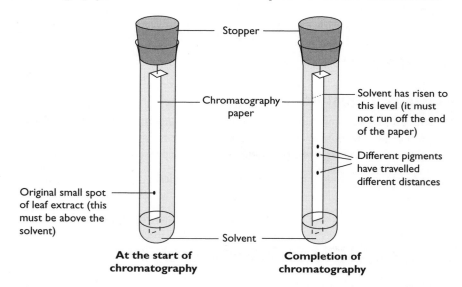

At the start of chromatography   **Completion of chromatography**

Key concepts you must understand

Sucrose does not react with Benedict's solution because the reactive parts of the molecules are 'unavailable' — they have already reacted (in the glycosidic bond). When the molecule is hydrolysed, these reactive portions become free to react.

In chromatography, the R_f value is the ratio of the distance travelled by the test substance to that travelled by the solvent front (distance travelled by substance/distance travelled by solvent front). The R_f value of a substance in a particular solvent at a particular temperature is constant, is unique to that substance and can be used to identify it. If the materials separated by chromatography are colourless, their position in the chromatogram can sometimes be found by using sprays that will 'colour' them or by making them radioactive (radioactive labelling) before attempting the separation.

What the examiners will expect you to be able to do

- Recall any of the key facts.
- Explain any of the key concepts.
- Use information concerning biochemical tests to identify substances in a mixture.
- Measure distances on drawings of chromatograms and calculate R_f values.
- Explain why an R_f value must always be less than 1.
- Describe the technique of paper chromatography.
- Complete diagrams showing condensation of glucose, amino acids and fatty acids and glycerol.
- Complete diagrams showing hydrolysis of maltose, sucrose, triglycerides and dipeptides.
- Identify, with reasons, individual polysaccharides from drawings of their molecules.
- Explain how polysaccharides are suited to their functions.
- In an unfamiliar situation, deduce, from information given, how the tertiary structure of a protein causes a certain reaction/function to take place.
- Explain why changing pH conditions or heating strongly can cause protein function to be impaired.

Links Many aspects of the specification require an understanding of biochemistry. The chemical reactions that take place in photosynthesis and respiration will be difficult to appreciate unless you have a basic understanding of the molecules themselves. There are other areas where an understanding of biochemistry is important. Digestion, protein synthesis and the formation of urea in the liver are examples. So, brace yourself, and learn some chemistry!

The nature and action of enzymes

All enzymes are globular proteins with a specific tertiary structure (but the reverse is not true — *not* all globular proteins are enzymes). Enzymes act as catalysts and are specific (they catalyse only one reaction). Factors such as temperature, pH and concentration of enzyme and substrate affect the effectiveness of the enzyme. Each has its own optimum combination of these factors at which it will work with maximum efficiency. All the reactions going on inside cells are catalysed by enzymes: they would proceed much too slowly without this catalysis.

Key facts you must know

Enzymes are globular proteins. They have a specific three-dimensional shape because of their unique tertiary structure. Part of the enzyme molecule is called the **active site**.

Tip Remember, only enzymes have active sites. If you find yourself writing about the 'active site' of a hormone, substrate, molecule in a plasma membrane where chemicals bind, then you are doing it wrong and you will lose marks!

Enzymes are catalysts (they speed up the rate of biochemical reactions without being altered themselves by the reaction). The active site of an enzyme is the part of the molecule that binds with the substrate molecules (the substances that actually react together) and causes the catalysis. When an enzyme binds with the substrate, it forms an **enzyme–substrate complex**. There are two hypotheses as to how enzyme–substrate complexes form: the lock-and-key hypothesis and the more recent induced-fit hypothesis.

Key concepts you must understand

The atoms in a molecule are held together by chemical bonds. For molecules to react, they must be facing the right way as only part of one molecule will actually react with part of the other molecule. If the correct parts are not facing each other, no reaction is possible. Before an actual reaction can occur, some of the existing bonds in the molecules must break so that new ones can form.

Take, for example, the hydrolysis of maltose to two molecules of α-glucose:

$$C_{12}H_{22}O_{11} + H_2O \longrightarrow C_6H_{12}O_6 + C_6H_{12}O_6$$

The stages of bond breaking and bond formation are shown in the diagrams below.

Bonds broken

New bonds form

Breaking bonds needs energy — this is called the **activation energy**. Once activated by bonds breaking, the maltose and water can react, new bonds form and two molecules of α-glucose are made. When the new bonds form, energy is released. The following diagram shows how the energy levels of the molecules involved change during the course of this reaction.

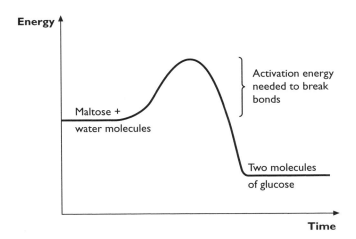

The activation energy can be supplied when two reacting molecules collide — if they collide hard enough and are facing the right way. Enzymes lower the activation energy needed by holding the molecules very close together and facing the right way. If a lot of activation energy is needed, not many of the molecules will have enough kinetic energy at normal temperatures. Reducing the activation energy needed means that more molecules have enough energy to react and the reaction is faster.

The **lock-and-key hypothesis** of enzyme action suggests that the active site of the enzyme and substrate molecules have complementary shapes — the shape of the substrate molecule fits into the shape of the active site like a key fits into a lock.

Tip Be careful not to describe the shapes of active site and substrate as the *same*. If they *were* the *same* they would not fit into each other.

Lock-and-key hypothesis

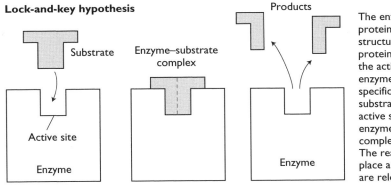

The enzyme is a protein. The tertiary structure of the protein results in the active site of the enzyme having a specific shape. The substrate fits the active site and an enzyme–substrate complex is formed. The reaction takes place and the products are released.

The **induced-fit hypothesis** suggests that, initially, the active site shape is not complementary to the shape of the substrate, but that as the correct substrate begins to bind, it causes (induces) the active site to change shape so that it does 'fit'.

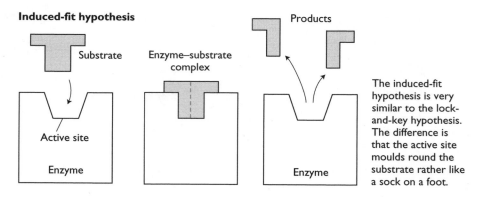

Induced-fit hypothesis

Substrate

Enzyme–substrate complex

Products

Active site

Enzyme

Enzyme

Enzyme

The induced-fit hypothesis is very similar to the lock-and-key hypothesis. The difference is that the active site moulds round the substrate rather like a sock on a foot.

Because enzymes are proteins, high temperatures denature them and, because the shape of the active site is changed, they cease to function.

Tip Don't write about heat *killing* enzymes. Enzymes (although crucial in living cells) are merely chemicals: they are not alive and so cannot be killed. If you insist on writing about killing enzymes in your examination it will be marked as wrong.

The number of substrate molecules that react by forming enzyme–substrate complexes in one second is called the enzyme **turnover rate** and is a measure of enzyme activity.

The optimum temperature of an enzyme is the temperature at which it catalyses the reaction most effectively — the temperature at which it has the highest turnover rate. Increasing the temperature gives particles more kinetic energy (they move around more). This means that enzyme and substrate are more likely to collide and this increases the rate of reaction. It also means, however, that the enzyme molecules start to denature, which decreases the rate of reaction. The optimum temperature is a 'trade-off' between these two effects. Up to this temperature, the effect of increased collisions is greater than the effect of denaturation. After this point the effect of denaturation is far greater and the turnover rate of the enzyme rapidly falls to zero. The actual optimum varies from enzyme to enzyme but, for most enzymes in mammals, the optimum is around 40°C.

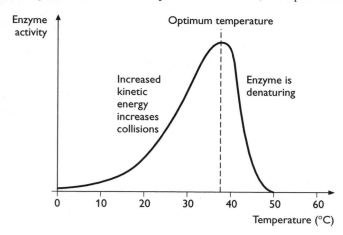

Extremes of pH can also denature enzymes by damaging the bonds that give the active site its shape. The denaturing effect is usually the same on either side of the optimum pH and so a graph relating pH to enzyme activity tends to be more symmetrical in shape than the temperature/enzyme activity graph.

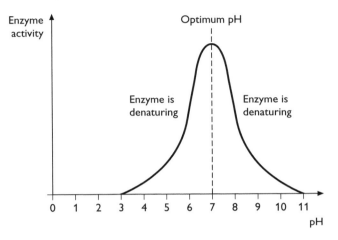

The concentration of the substrate will affect the rate of reaction as it affects how many enzyme–substrate complexes can form per second at a given temperature. Increasing the substrate concentration will increase the rate of reaction until the maximum turnover rate for that temperature, pH and enzyme concentration is reached. (If the active sites are all occupied at any time, saturation has occurred.)

Factor affecting enzyme activity	How the factor produces the effect	Result	Limit
Temperature	Increasing temperature increases kinetic energy of enzyme and substrate molecules	More collisions and so more enzyme–substrate complexes form and rate increases	Above a critical temperature enzyme is denatured and so reaction ceases
pH	pH too far from the optimum — breaks bonds in active site	At optimum pH maximum number of enzyme–substrate complexes form	Away from optimum pH denaturation of enzyme occurs
Substrate concentration	More substrate molecules means increased chance of collisions occurring	More collisions and so more enzyme–substrate complexes form and rate increases	Above a certain concentration, all active sites are in use — rate cannot increase further without more enzyme, higher temperature or more favourable pH

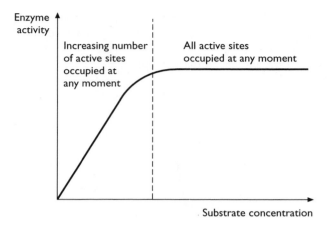

Competitive inhibitors have molecules very similar in shape to the substrate molecules (those that bind with the active site of an enzyme). Because of this similarity they can 'compete' with the substrate molecules for the active site and prevent them from binding to it, reducing the activity of the enzyme. The extent to which a competitive inhibitor reduces enzyme activity depends on the proportions of inhibitor molecules and substrate molecules. If there are three times as many substrate molecules as inhibitor molecules, the substrate molecules are three times as likely to bind with an active site. Put another way, 75% of the active sites will bind with substrate molecules and 25% will bind with inhibitor molecules. 25% of the active sites are not available to catalyse the reaction, so the enzyme activity (turnover rate) is decreased by 25%. A ratio of 3 inhibitor molecules to 1 substrate molecule would reduce enzyme activity by 75%. The graph below shows this in more detail.

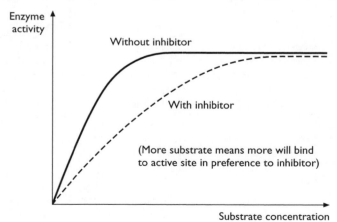

Non-competitive inhibitors bind with other parts of the enzyme and cause a change in shape of the active site so that it will not bind with its substrate. The effect of non-competitive inhibitors is largely independent of the substrate concentration — as long as there are enough inhibitor molecules to bind with the all the enzyme molecules, their effect will be 100% inhibition. If there is enough inhibitor to bind with 75% of active sites, there will be 75% inhibition (as in the graph below).

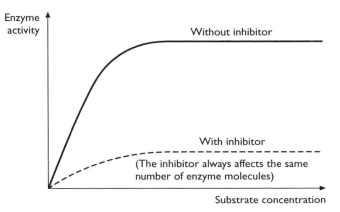

Most competitive and non-competitive inhibitors are reversible inhibitors.

What the examiners will expect you to be able to do

- Recall any of the key facts.
- Explain any of the key concepts.
- From graphs of enzyme activity, deduce whether the graph is showing the effect of:
  - temperature
  - competitive inhibitor
  - substrate concentration
  - pH
  - non-competitive inhibitor

Tip You must learn to recognise the shapes of these graphs and understand why they are the shape they are.

- Deduce from graphs where changing a factor is limiting enzyme activity and where changing the factor is having no effect. If a factor is limiting enzyme activity, then increasing it will increase the activity. If an increase produces no effect on the activity of the enzyme, then the factor is non-limiting and something else must be limiting the reaction.

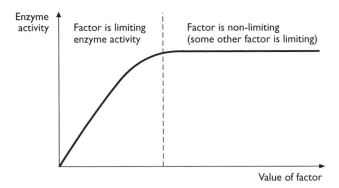

- Realise that because enzymes speed up reactions at normal temperatures, using enzymes in industrial applications can save a lot of energy (to heat the reactants where no enzyme is used) and therefore a lot of money.

Tip Examiners will *not* expect you to know any specific examples, but you may be asked to deduce advantages of using enzymes in industrial applications from information given.

Links You should appreciate that every single chemical reaction that occurs in an organism is controlled by a specific enzyme. Because of this, any factor affecting enzymes will affect the rate of these reactions and the biological processes of which they are part. The graph showing the effect of temperature on photosynthesis is exactly the same shape as the graph showing the effect of temperature on enzyme activity. At temperatures above their optimum, the enzymes controlling the reactions of photosynthesis denature rapidly and the process soon grinds to a halt.

Biological processes often contain many steps and can be represented as:

$$A \longrightarrow B \longrightarrow C \longrightarrow D$$

All the stages in this process are controlled by enzymes and so if *any* of the enzymes is inhibited, the whole process will stop. Controlling the activity of enzymes is one way in which biological processes can be 'switched' on and off.

Tissues, organs and systems

This section looks at the way in which cells are organised in multicellular organisms. Similar cells are grouped into tissues that are arranged into organs. Sometimes, several organs are linked into an organ system.

Key facts you must know

A **tissue** is a group of similar cells all performing the same function.

An **epithelium** is a tissue that covers an organ (sometimes, if it lines the inside of an organ, it is called an **endothelium**). Substances entering or leaving the cells of the organ must first pass through the epithelium and so these epithelia have special features that adapt them for efficient exchange of materials.

Epithelia adapted for exchange can be found lining the small intestine and making up the walls of the alveoli in the lungs.

Simple epithelia are made of just one layer of cells: stratified epithelia contain several layers of cells.

The alveolar epithelium is a type of simple epithelium called **squamous epithelium**. The cells of the alveolar epithelium are flat and thin: they have no cilia or other surface features. The cells of the alveolar epithelium 'sit' on a thin layer of non-living tissue called the basement membrane. The basement membrane helps to hold the cells together.

Blood is an unusual tissue because it moves and it contains *several* types of cells suspended in a liquid (the plasma). The cells found in the liquid plasma are:

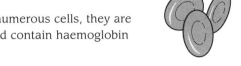

- **red blood cells** — by far the most numerous cells, they are biconcave discs with no nucleus and contain haemoglobin to carry oxygen around the body

- **lymphocytes** — white blood cells that either produce antibodies (B lymphocytes) or kill infected cells directly (T lymphocytes). They are about the same size as red blood cells and have a large, round nucleus

- **monocytes** — white blood cells that can squeeze their way out of capillaries to engulf pathogens by phagocytosis. They are about twice the diameter of red blood cells and have a C-shaped or horseshoe-shaped nucleus

- **granulocytes** — large, white blood cells involved in phago-cytosis. They have multi-lobed nuclei and granular cytoplasm

Tip You will not need to know the functions of these white blood cells in any detail for the unit test, but you must be able to identify them from drawings or photographs. This is quite easy if you can recognise a red blood cell. You can then use the size of a red blood cell as a starting point.

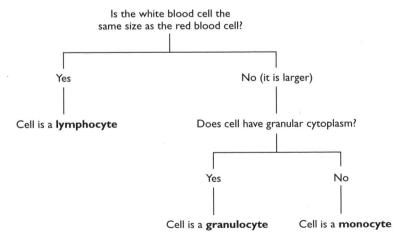

Organs are structures that contain several tissues, each performing a different function but all contributing to the overall functioning of the organ. The heart, arteries, arteri-oles, veins and venules are organs because they contain more than one type of tissue in a single structure.

Key concepts you must understand

The plasma membrane is the exchange surface of a cell.

As cells get bigger, the volume increases faster than the surface area, so the surface area-to-volume ratio decreases. We can prove this mathematically:
- pretend that the cell is a cube with each side being 1 arbitrary unit (au) long — the surface area of each side is therefore $1 \times 1 = 1$ au^2
- there are six sides to a cube, so the total surface area is 6 au^2
- the volume is $1 \times 1 \times 1 = 1$ au^3
- the ratio of surface area to volume = $6/1 = 6$
- for a cubic cell with sides 2 au long, total surface area = $6 \times 2 \times 2 = 24$ au^2 and the volume = $2 \times 2 \times 2 = 8$ au^3, so the ratio is now $24/8 = 3$ — it has decreased
- if you do the sums for cubes with sides of 4 au and 8 au, you will find that the surface area to volume ratios are 1.5 and 0.75 respectively

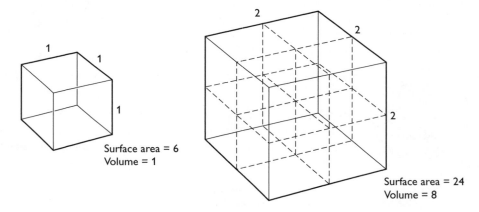

Surface area = 6
Volume = 1

Surface area = 24
Volume = 8

Above a certain size, exchange through the plasma membrane becomes inefficient and this therefore limits the size of the cell. Using oxygen uptake by a cell as an example:
- the area of the cell surface determines (in large part) how much oxygen the cell can obtain (the supply rate)
- the volume of the cell determines (in large part) how much oxygen the cell needs (the demand)
- the ratio of surface area to volume decreases as a cell gets bigger and so, above a certain size, the plasma membrane of a cell would not be able to supply enough oxygen for the increased volume of the cell (demand would outstrip supply), so this limits cell size

Red blood cells are specialised to carry out the function of carrying oxygen around the body. They have a number of adaptations:
- having no nucleus means that more haemoglobin can be packed in the cell
- the biconcave disc shape creates a large surface area for diffusion of oxygen into and out of the cell and (because it is thin) also ensures a short diffusion distance from the centre of the cell

- a flexible plasma membrane allows the red blood cells to change shape and be squeezed through the narrowest capillaries

The heart is a good example of an organ as it contains:

- cardiac muscle, which makes up the bulk of the tissue in the heart and generates the force to pump the blood
- blood in blood vessels in the wall of the heart, which carries oxygen and glucose to all the muscle cells so that they are able to respire to release the ATP for contraction of the cardiac muscle
- valves (made from connective tissue) to help ensure one-way flow within the heart
- Purkyne tissue carries impulses through the heart, which causes the contraction of cardiac muscle cells

All the tissues are necessary for the heart to function effectively.

Arteries, arterioles and veins are also examples of organs. They contain:

- an outer layer made from tough fibrous tissue to prevent damage
- a middle layer containing muscle and elastic tissue (especially in arteries and arterioles) to allow stretching and recoil of the wall with the changes in pressure of the blood
- an inner endothelium which provides a smooth lining (to provide little resistance to blood flow) and which, in veins, is modified in places to form valves

Again, all these tissues are necessary for the blood vessels to carry out their functions.

The heart, arteries and veins together make up the circulatory system. Several organs are integrated into a system with one major function — circulation.

What the examiners will expect you to be able to do

- Recall any of the key facts.
- Explain any of the key concepts.
- Identify, with reasons, different types of blood cell from a drawing or a photograph.
- Deduce, from information given, whether a structure is a tissue or an organ. For example, what is a cancer? How would you classify it? Most cancers are made of large groups of identical cells, so is it a tissue? If so, it is not one of our normal tissues.
- Realise that epithelial cells often get damaged because of their position, and so must be replaced constantly.

Links The terms 'tissue' and 'organ' will be used repeatedly throughout your biology course and you need to appreciate what is being described and why particular terms are being used. You will need to appreciate the difference between bone tissue and **a bone** (e.g. your femur) which is an organ. The same applies to muscle tissue and **a muscle** (e.g. your tricep) as well as to nervous tissue and **a nerve** (e.g. your vagus nerve). Each muscle and each nerve is an organ. Why not try and find out why?

The circulatory and breathing systems at rest and during exercise

This section looks at the circulatory system and the breathing system and also the way in which they function as a coupled unit — that is, the way in which they work together to deliver oxygen to the tissues and remove carbon dioxide from the body. The structure of the heart is related to its working and the structure of the blood vessels is related to their ability to perform their various functions. The fine structure of the lungs is related to gas exchange. The nervous control of the two systems keeps a basic rhythm of breathing and a basic heart rate. Exercise increases cardiac output and pulmonary ventilation supplying extra oxygen to, and removing extra carbon dioxide from, increasingly active muscles.

The circulatory system — the heart

Key facts you must know

You must be able to identify the parts of the heart shown on the diagram below and be aware of their functions.

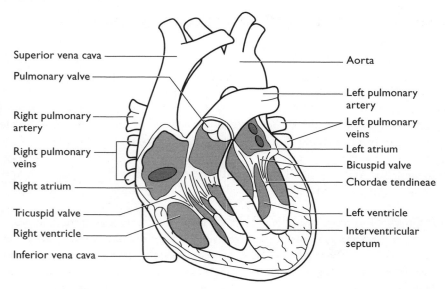

You must recognise the general pattern of the circulatory system and be able to identify the blood vessels shown on the following diagram.

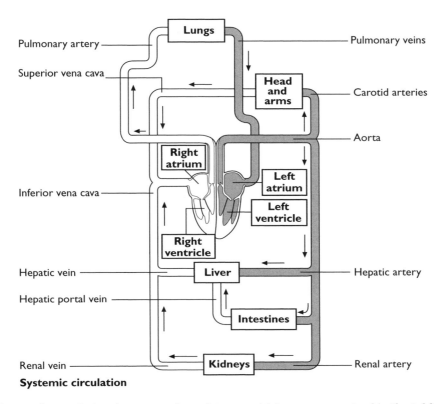

Pulmonary artery — Lungs — Pulmonary veins

Superior vena cava

Head and arms — Carotid arteries

Aorta

Right atrium

Inferior vena cava — Left atrium

Left ventricle

Right ventricle

Hepatic vein — Liver — Hepatic artery

Hepatic portal vein — Intestines

Renal vein — Kidneys — Renal artery

Systemic circulation

The cardiac cycle involves a number of stages which are summarised in the table and diagrams below.

Stage	Action of atria	Result	Action of ventricles	Result
(1) Atrial systole	Walls contract	Blood forced through valves into ventricles	Walls relax	Fill with blood
(2) Ventricular systole	Walls relax	Blood neither enters nor leaves	Walls contract	(a) No blood leaves, but pressure of blood in ventricles increases (b) Pressure of blood opens valves and blood is ejected into main arteries
(3) Ventricular diastole	Walls relax	(a) Blood enters atria but cannot pass into ventricles as valves still closed (b) Blood enters atria and passes into ventricles — valves now open	Walls relax	(a) Blood neither enters nor leaves (b) Blood enters from atria 'passive ventricular filling' — not due to atrial contraction

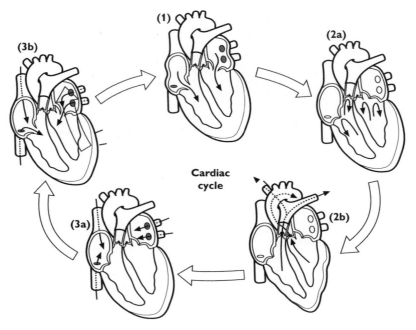

Cardiac cycle

The heart beat is **myogenic**: it originates in the heart itself (at the sino-atrial (SA) node).

Tip Don't explain the term 'myogenic' by saying that the heart beat does not originate outside the heart — say precisely where it does originate.

Special fibres of Purkyne tissue conduct impulses from the SA node to all parts of the heart, causing contraction of the cardiac muscle.

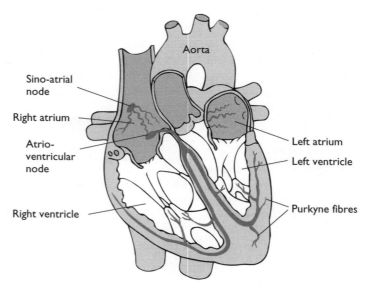

The only route for the impulse to pass from atria to ventricles is by conduction through the atrio-ventricular (AV) node that conducts very slowly. As a result:
- the impulse is held up
- after the delay, the impulse passes quickly through the Purkyne fibres to all parts of the ventricles
- the ventricles contract some time after the atria

Although the SA node initiates the impulses causing contractions of the chambers, the *rate* of impulse generation (and therefore the rate of heart beat) can be affected by nerve impulses from the cardiovascular centre in the medulla. Sympathetic impulses (carried by the cardiac nerve) increase the rate and parasympathetic impulses (carried by the vagus nerve) decrease the rate. The hormone **adrenaline** binds to receptors in the SA node and increases the rate of impulse generation.

The amount of blood pumped by the ventricles in one minute is called the cardiac output. The cardiac output depends on:
- the amount of blood pumped in one beat (the stroke volume)
- the number of beats per minute (the heart rate)

So, cardiac output = stroke volume × heart rate.

Key concepts you must understand

Mammals have a double circulation which has a number of advantages:
- by keeping the pulmonary and systemic circulations separate, blood passing to the tissues is always saturated with oxygen
- because the blood is pumped twice by the heart, it is delivered to the tissues at high pressure, which makes for a more efficient circulation

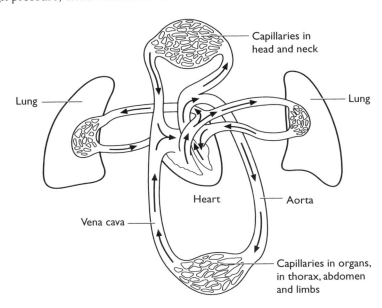

Capillaries in head and neck

Lung

Lung

Heart

Aorta

Vena cava

Capillaries in organs, in thorax, abdomen and limbs

The events of the cardiac cycle create changes in volume and pressure in the chambers of the heart which cause the opening and closing of valves and the movement of blood. The diagram below shows the changes in pressure for the blood in the left side of the heart and aorta together with the changes in volume of the ventricle.

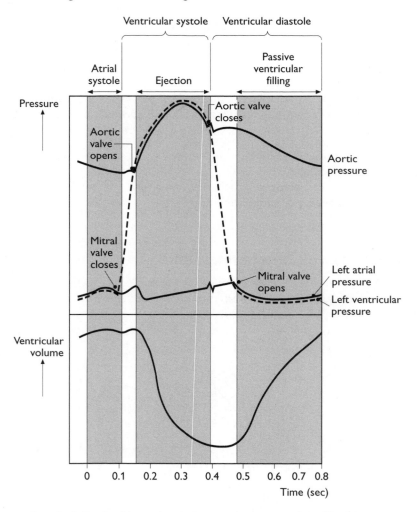

Tip Remember the following ideas when you try to interpret a chart like this:
- the mitral (bicuspid) valve opens when the blood pressure in the atrium is greater than in the ventricle and closes when the pressures are reversed
- the aortic valve opens when the blood pressure in the ventricle is greater than in the aorta and closes when the pressures are reversed
- blood is a *fluid* and will *flow* from a high pressure region to a low pressure region

Note that the pulmonary circulation is a low-pressure circulation and a chart for the right side of the heart shows an identical shape, but the pressures are lower.

Because of the events of the cardiac cycle, blood leaves the *heart* in *pulses* when the ventricles eject blood — but the blood flow through the *system* is *continuous*, i.e. there is no 'gap' until the heart squirts out the next bit of blood because of the stretch and recoil of the arteries.

What the examiners will expect you to be able to do

- Recall any of the key facts.
- Explain any of the key concepts.
- Identify stages in the cardiac cycle from diagrams.
- Given information about the condition of the walls of the chambers of the heart or the pressure of blood in the chambers, deduce whether the valves will be open or closed.
- Complete the labelling of diagrams of the heart and circulatory system.
- Calculate cardiac output from data on heart rate and stroke volume.
- Explain, from data supplied, the effects of certain chemicals/drugs on the heart rate. You may be given information about a drug that stimulates the SA node or prevents the normal stimulation of the SA node and be asked to explain the effect on the heart rate.
- Identify and explain events in a pressure/volume chart of the cardiac cycle. You may be asked to pinpoint when the mitral valve opens or the period when blood will pass from left atrium to left ventricle and explain this in terms of pressure differences.

The circulatory system — the blood vessels

Key facts you must know

The main types of blood vessel are arteries (and small arteries called arterioles), capillaries and veins.

The structure of the blood vessels is related to their function. They have some features in common, such as:
- they are all tubular — the ideal shape for transporting liquids (you won't see many square hose pipes because the 'corners' would create too much resistance to the flow)
- they all have a tough outer layer to prevent damage (except the microscopic capillaries)

Arteries, arterioles, capillaries and veins each have some features that adapt them to their particular functions. These are shown in the following table.

Feature	Artery	Arteriole	Capillary	Vein
Cross-section of vessel	Thick wall and narrow lumen	Thinner wall, but relatively more muscle	Microscopic vessels, wall one cell thick	Valves, thin wall, little muscle, large lumen
Blood flow	To an organ, away from heart	Within an organ, to capillaries in different parts of the organ	Around cells of the organ	Away from an organ, towards the heart
Type of blood	Oxygenated*	Oxygenated*	Blood becomes deoxygenated	Deoxygenated*
Blood pressure	High and in pulses (pulsatile)	Not quite as high and less pulsatile	Pressure drops throughout capillary network	Low and non-pulsatile
Main functions of vessels	Transport of blood to an organ	Transport in an organ; redistribution of blood	Formation of tissue fluid to allow exchange between blood and cells of an organ	Transport of blood back to heart
Adaptations to the main function	Large amount of elastic tissue in wall allows stretching due to pulses (surges in blood pressure) and recoil after pulses; endothelium forms a smooth layer to give least resistance	Large amount of smooth muscle under nervous control to allow redistribution of blood: constriction limits blood flow to an area; dilation increases blood flow; constriction of *all* arterioles increases resistance and blood pressure	Small size allows an extensive network close to all cells of an organ; thin permeable ('leaky') wall allows formation of tissue fluid for exchange with surrounding cells	Large lumen and thin wall offer least resistance to flow as blood is under low pressure; valves prevent backflow of blood

* Except the pulmonary and umbilical blood vessels

Key concepts you must understand

Ejection of the blood by the ventricles contracting creates a high pressure pulse of blood (the systolic pressure) followed by lower pressure (the diastolic pressure) as the ventricles relax.

Ejection of blood stretches the arteries (those near the heart in particular), and they absorb the pressure created by the ventricles. When they recoil, pressure is once again exerted on the blood — the arteries are acting as 'secondary pumps' and keep the blood flowing smoothly.

When the arteries are stretched, not all the pressure they absorb is 're-applied' when they recoil — some is lost. Because of this (and also because of losses due to resistance from the artery walls):

- the systolic and diastolic pressures decrease further away from the heart
- the differences between systolic and diastolic pressures decrease further away from the heart, until the blood flow is not pulsatile but even

Tip When you feel a pulse at your wrist, be clear about what it is — it is *not* a surge of *blood*. It is a kind of 'shock wave' of high pressure resulting from blood being ejected from the left ventricle. It takes time for the pressure wave to be transmitted through the blood and so, following each ejection, pulses are felt earlier nearer the heart and later further away.

Tissue fluid is the liquid that surrounds the cells and is the means by which substances are exchanged between the blood and surrounding cells.

- Tissue fluid is lost from the blood in the capillary networks because the high hydrostatic pressure of blood entering the capillaries forces substances through the permeable (leaky) walls.
- The composition of tissue fluid is determined by the size of the 'gaps' in the capillary wall — anything small enough to pass through will do so. In practice, this means that blood cells and most proteins do not escape from the blood, but molecules smaller than this do escape.
- Some tissue fluid later returns to the blood so there is exchange between the blood and the surrounding cells.

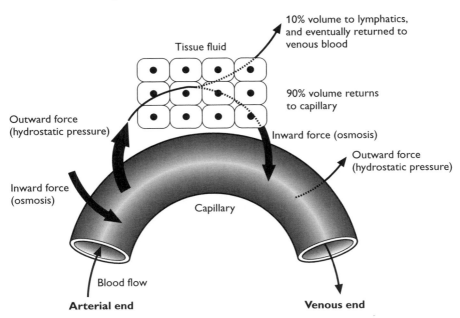

What the examiners will expect you to be able to do

- Recall any of the key facts.
- Explain any of the key concepts.
- Relate the structure of the blood vessels to their function from information given.
- Interpret charts showing the blood pressure in the various blood vessels and explain changes in terms of the structure of the blood vessels.
- Interpret diagrams of tissue fluid circulation, deducing, from pressures given, where tissue fluid will be formed and where it will return to the blood.

The breathing system

Key facts you must know

You must know the main structures in the breathing system.

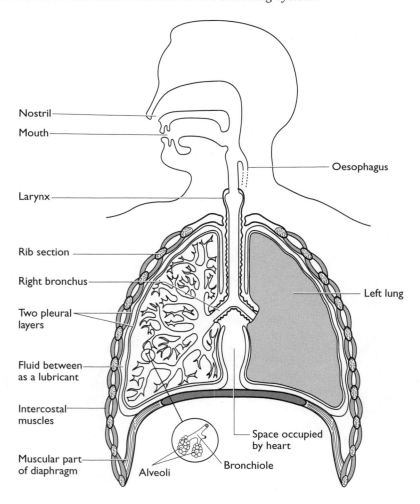

Nostril

Mouth

Oesophagus

Larynx

Rib section

Right bronchus

Two pleural layers

Left lung

Fluid between as a lubricant

Intercostal muscles

Space occupied by heart

Muscular part of diaphragm

Alveoli

Bronchiole

Tip Remember, we breathe in *air* (not oxygen), and we breathe out *air* (not carbon dioxide).

Gas exchange takes place in the alveoli (not just 'the lungs').

Oxygen diffuses from the alveolar air into red blood cells and carbon dioxide diffuses from the blood plasma into the alveoli.

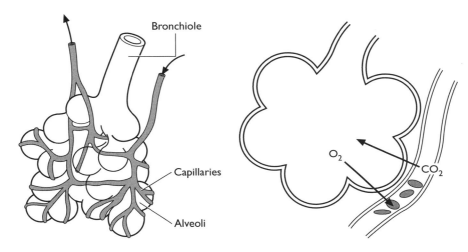

The composition of inhaled and exhaled air differs in a number of key respects as a result of gas exchange in the alveoli, as shown in the following table.

Gas	% in inhaled air	% in exhaled air
Oxygen	21	17
Carbon dioxide	0.04	4
Nitrogen and inert gases	79	78.6
Water vapour	Variable	Saturated

To breathe in (inspire/inhale):
- the external intercostal muscles contract and raise the ribs
- the muscle of the diaphragm contracts and pulls the diaphragm downwards
- these two movements increase the volume of the thorax
- the pressure in the thorax decreases
- air moves in from a higher pressure region outside the body

To breathe out (expire/exhale):
- the external intercostal muscles relax and the ribs fall under gravity
- the muscle of the diaphragm relaxes and the diaphragm resumes its dome shape
- these two movements reduce the volume of the thorax
- the pressure in the thorax increases
- air moves out from the higher pressure region inside the body

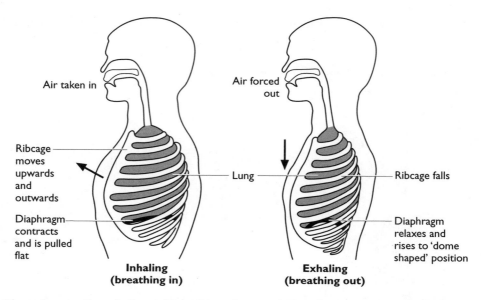

**Inhaling
(breathing in)**   **Exhaling
(breathing out)**

There is a resting rhythm of breathing that produces about 12–15 inspirations and expirations per minute.

This natural rhythm is controlled by the respiratory centre in the medulla oblongata, which contains an inspiratory centre and an expiratory centre.

Impulses from stretch receptors in the thorax passing to the inspiratory centre are the main stimulus for the natural breathing rhythm.

The respiratory centre sends impulses to the diaphragm along the phrenic nerve and to the intercostal muscles along the thoracic nerve.

Key concepts you must understand

Gas exchange in the alveoli is very efficient because:
- collectively, alveoli present a large surface area
- the diffusion distance through a cell in the alveolus wall and then through a cell in the capillary wall is very short
- there is a large difference in the concentration of oxygen between the alveolar air and the blood
- alveoli are moist

Concentrations of gases are often expressed as partial pressures of the gases. This allows a comparison between concentration of a gas in a mixture of gases (the air) and dissolved in a liquid (the blood). Partial pressures are expressed in kiloPascals (kPa).

The difference in partial pressures of oxygen and carbon dioxide between alveolar air and blood is maintained by ventilation and circulation:
- ventilation continually replaces the air in the alveoli with atmospheric air that has a high partial pressure of oxygen and a low partial pressure of carbon dioxide

- circulation removes newly oxygenated blood from the capillary next to the alveolus and replaces it with deoxygenated blood (the partial pressure of oxygen in this blood is lower than in air; the partial pressure of carbon dioxide is higher than in air)

The moist lining of the alveoli is particularly important in ensuring the efficient diffusion of carbon dioxide:
- the partial pressure of carbon dioxide in the blood is only slightly greater than that of the alveolar air
- carbon dioxide is much more soluble than oxygen and so can dissolve quickly in the moist lining, speeding up diffusion

Moving air into and out of the lungs is called ventilation and it depends on changing the pressure in the thorax. This is possible only because the diaphragm and pleural membranes completely surround the lungs, making the thorax completely airtight.

The basic rhythm of breathing is controlled by the respiratory centre as shown in the flow chart below. The expiratory centre plays little part; it is mainly controlled by the inspiratory centre.

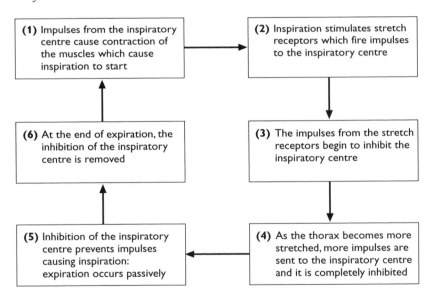

Pulmonary ventilation is the amount of oxygen breathed in one minute. It depends on:
- the amount of air breathed in with each breath (the tidal volume)
- the number of breaths per minute

So, pulmonary ventilation = tidal volume × breathing rate.

Tip Pulmonary ventilation is a similar concept to cardiac output. Both describe the amount of a fluid (air or blood) moved per minute. Both depend on the volume of fluid moved per cycle of the pumping mechanism (tidal volume or stroke volume) and the number of cycles per minute (breathing rate or heart rate).

What the examiners will expect you to be able to do

- Recall any of the key facts.
- Explain any of the key concepts.
- Explain how the structure of the lung ensures a short diffusion distance for gas exchange.
- Explain how the structure of the lung ensures a large surface area for gas exchange.
- Explain how maximum concentration difference for gas exchange is maintained.
- Identify structures in drawings or photographs of lung tissue.
- Identify key structures or processes in flow charts representing breathing movements.
- Calculate and explain pulmonary ventilation rates.
- Interpret data on partial pressures of gases to explain normal or altered gas exchange in the alveoli.

The effects of exercise

Key facts you must know

During exercise, many muscles are more active and must respire faster to release the extra energy (ATP) required. The increased respiration rate demands more oxygen and more glucose. Increased pulmonary ventilation brings more air into the lungs per minute; increased cardiac output results in the blood collecting more oxygen from the lungs and more glucose from the liver and transporting these to the muscles. Increased cardiac output is achieved by increasing the stroke volume and the heart rate (the heart beats stronger and faster). Increased pulmonary ventilation is achieved by increasing the tidal volume and breathing rate (we breathe deeper and faster).

Tip You can easily remember what happens if you just think about your own body during exercise. You can *feel* your pulse and heart beat more easily during exercise — the heart *must* be beating with more force (increased stroke volume) as well as the more obvious increase in rate. Similarly, you can *feel* and *see* breathing movements more easily — they *must* be *deeper* as well as faster.

Redistribution of the blood means that a much higher proportion of blood passes to the muscles and less passes to organs such as the skin and intestines. The amount of blood passing to the kidneys and brain remains unaltered.

Tip You must distinguish carefully between *proportion* of blood and *amount* of blood. During exercise the *amount* of blood passing to the kidneys and brain remains unaltered, but it is a smaller *proportion* of the increased cardiac output.

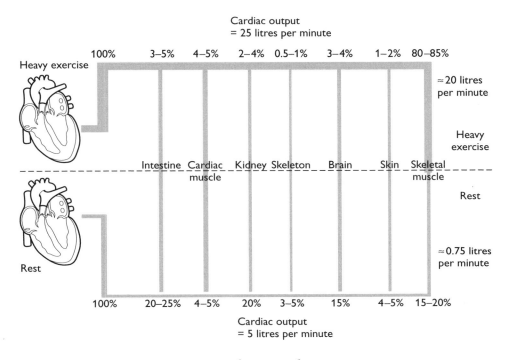

Key concepts you must understand

All the changes that occur in the circulatory and breathing systems during exercise are designed to deliver more blood carrying more oxygen to the muscles. At the same time:

- the brain must continue to function normally and so must receive the same amount of blood
- the kidneys must continue to excrete urea at the same rate and so must receive the same amount of blood

The increases in pulmonary ventilation and cardiac output are related to the intensity of the exercise. The main stimulus that increases cardiac output and pulmonary ventilation is the increased level of carbon dioxide in the blood plasma (from the increased respiration of the muscles). This increased level of carbon dioxide is detected by chemoreceptors in the aortic arch, carotid artery and the medulla. This results in increased impulses from these receptors to the cardiovascular centre and to the respiratory centre.

In the cardiovascular centre, increased impulses from the chemoreceptors lead to more impulses being fired along the sympathetic nerve (cardiac nerve) to the SA node and heart rate is increased. The increased return of blood to the heart stimulates an increase in stroke volume. In the respiratory centre, the increased impulses from the chemoreceptors result in more impulses being fired along the phrenic nerve and breathing rate is increased. When carbon dioxide levels fall after exercise, cardiac output and pulmonary ventilation fall.

Tip Cardiac output and pulmonary ventilation do not drop like a stone at the end of exercise. Carbon dioxide is still being produced from the oxidation of lactic acid formed during the exercise. As this gradually decreases, so too do the impulses from the chemoreceptors and, therefore, the number of impulses from the cardiovascular and respiratory centres.

Blood is redistributed by the dilation and constriction of appropriate arterioles. Those to the skin and intestines are constricted (to reduce blood flow) while those to the muscles are dilated (to increase blood flow).

What the examiners will expect you to be able to do

- Recall any of the key facts.
- Explain any of the key concepts.
- Interpret and explain diagrams and data showing changes in blood distribution during exercise.
- Interpret and explain diagrams and data showing changes in rate and depth of breathing during exercise.
- Calculate changes in heart and breathing rates during exercise from data supplied.
- Explain changes in gas exchange rates from data supplied of partial pressures.

Tip Remember, partial pressures are measures of concentrations of gases, and rate of diffusion is, in part, determined by the difference in concentrations.

Links Most of the material in this particular section will only be tested in the Unit 1 test. The main links occur within the module with processes such as diffusion and osmosis, Fick's law and structure/size of molecules. There are, however, links with other areas, particularly those covering other gas exchange surfaces, the transport of respiratory gases in more detail as well as the chemistry of aerobic and anaerobic respiration.

This section contains questions similar in style to those you can expect to see in your Unit 1 examination. The limited number of questions means that it is impossible to cover all the topics and all the question styles, but they should give you a flavour of what to expect. The responses that are shown are real students' answers to the questions.

There are several ways of using this section. You could:

- 'hide' the answers to each question and try the question yourself. It needn't be a memory test — use your notes to see if you can actually make all the points you ought to make
- check your answers against the candidates' responses and make an estimate of the likely standard of your response to each question
- check your answers against the examiner's comments to see if you can appreciate where you might have lost marks
- check your answers against the terms used in the question — did you *explain* when you were asked to, or did you merely *describe*?

Examiner's comments

All candidate responses are followed by examiner's comments. These are preceded by the icon 🇪 and indicate where credit is due. In the weaker answers, they also point out areas for improvement, specific problems and common errors such as lack of clarity, weak or non-existent development, irrelevance, misinterpretation of the question and mistaken meanings of terms.

The breathing system and diffusion

(a) Figure 1 shows the structure of the human gas exchange system.

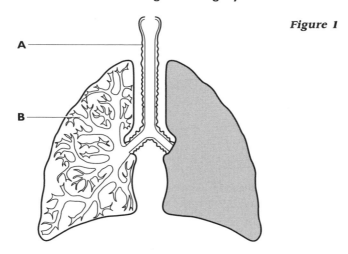

Figure 1

A

B

    (i) Name the structures labelled **A** and **B**.   (1 mark)

    (ii) What causes air to move into the lungs as the ribs are lifted upwards and
        outwards and the diaphragm contracts?   (1 mark)

(b) Gas exchange occurs in the alveoli. Equal volumes of oxygen and carbon dioxide
diffuse in opposite directions through the wall of the alveolus and the wall of the
capillary. Both walls are thin and moist. Carbon dioxide is much more soluble in
water than oxygen. Figure 2 represents the partial pressures of the two gases
which exist in the alveoli and in the blood.

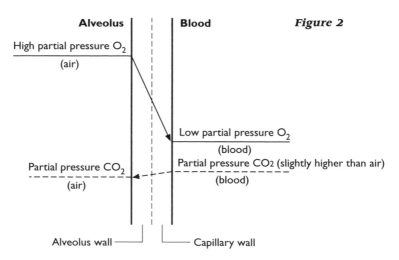

Alveolus   Blood   *Figure 2*

High partial pressure O_2
(air)

Low partial pressure O_2
(blood)

Partial pressure CO_2 Partial pressure CO_2 (slightly higher than air)
(air)   (blood)

Alveolus wall   Capillary wall

question

(i) **Suggest why it seems unlikely that equal volumes of the two gases will diffuse through the walls of the alveolus and capillary. Explain your answer.** (2 marks)

(ii) **Suggest the importance of the moist surfaces in ensuring that equal volumes of the two gases do diffuse through the walls.** (2 marks)

Total: 6 marks

■ ■ ■

Candidates' answers to Question 1

Candidate A
(a) (i) A — trachea; B — bronchus

Candidate B
(a) (i) A — trachea; B — bronchiole

> *e* Candidate A loses the mark as he or she has incorrectly written 'bronchus' instead of 'bronchiole'. Make sure that you know the difference between them. There are only two bronchi (right and left) which branch from the trachea, but thousands of bronchioles. Also remember, if a name ends in -iole it is a smaller version of some other structure — e.g. arter*iole* is a small artery

Candidate A
(a) (ii) Air moves in due to the pressure changes. The thorax volume increases, so the pressure in the thorax is less than the atmospheric pressure, so air moves into the lungs until the pressure is equalised.

Candidate B
(a) (ii) The volume of the thorax is increased and therefore the pressure decreases to less than atmospheric pressure, so air enters the lung and inflates the alveoli until pressure is equal to the atmospheric pressure.

> *e* Both candidates score the 1 mark available here, but have written far more than they needed to: it is the decrease in pressure that makes air move in — which is all it was necessary to say. Writing too much costs you valuable time.

Candidate A
(b) (i) Because the diffusion gradients between the alveolus and blood for the two gases are not equal. The oxygen gradient is steeper.

Candidate B
(b) (i) Because oxygen is going down a much steeper diffusion gradient and therefore will diffuse much quicker than the CO_2. Also because CO_2 is more soluble, it will diffuse through the walls easier because they are moist.

> *e* Candidate B has made it clear that the gradient for oxygen is steeper than for carbon dioxide and that the rate of diffusion depends on the gradient. Candidate A clearly understands that diffusion is involved and that gradients are important, but

has not made it clear how the gradient will affect diffusion rate, which results in the loss of 1 mark. **Remember that the examiner will not assume anything for you**.

Candidate A

(b) (ii) The carbon dioxide is more soluble than oxygen and so will dissolve in the moist layer of the alveolus.

Candidate B

(b) (ii) CO_2 is much more soluble in the moist surface but it has a shallow diffusion gradient and the lack of solubility of oxygen is compensated for by its steep diffusion gradient, therefore equal volumes of the gases are diffused through.

Both candidates clearly appreciate that the solubility of the gases is important in aiding passage across the wall of the alveolus. However, Candidate B makes it quite clear that increased solubility can compensate for a shallow diffusion gradient and scores 2 marks, whereas Candidate A makes no reference to this and gains only 1 mark. When you are deducing answers from new material, it helps to apply the 'so what?' test. If Candidate A had re-read his or her answer and said 'so what', he or she might have gone on to give more detail.

This question contains sections of different difficulty. Examiners would expect both grade A and grade C candidates to score full marks for part (a). They would also expect grade C candidates to score the marks in part (b) which directly uses the information presented. Grade A candidates would also go on to explain mechanisms.

Cell structure

The stages in cell fractionation are shown in Figure 1.

Figure 1

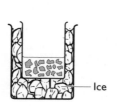  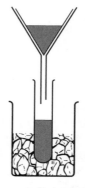 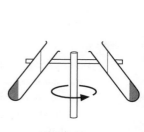

Tissue cut into small pieces and placed in isotonic solution — Ice

Tissue put into blender/homogeniser to break up whole cell

Mixture filtered to remove debris

Filtrate spun in centrifuge

(a) (i) Spinning the centrifuge at different speeds causes different organelles to settle out. Describe how you would alter the centrifuge settings to obtain, first, nuclei (only) and then mitochondria (only). You do not need to give actual speeds of centrifugation.

(3 marks)

(ii) Why must the tissue be placed in an isotonic solution rather than distilled water?

(2 marks)

(b) In an investigation into photosynthesis, palisade cells were 'fed' carbon dioxide containing radioactive carbon. How could cell fractionation be used to show that it is the chloroplasts in a palisade cell which use carbon dioxide to synthesise carbohydrates.

(3 marks)

Total: 8 marks

■ ■ ■

Candidates' answers to Question 2

Candidate A

(a) (i) The nucleus would be spun out at a lower speed than the mitochondrion, as it is larger so less speed is needed for it to settle. To get only the nuclei you would then extract the settled out nuclei before spinning the filtrate again at a lower speed.

Candidate B

(a) (i) Start off with a low speed and draw off the supernatant to remove the nuclei. A medium speed can then be used and when the supernatant is removed, mitochondria will be left.

e Candidate B has produced a comprehensive answer describing fully the technique required, although the principle behind it (difference in size/mass) is not mentioned. This is enough, however, to get full marks. Candidate A also seems to understand it, but contradicts him or herself concerning the relative speeds at which the two organelles will settle out. One mark is therefore lost. **Check that you don't contradict yourself in your answers.**

Candidate A

(a) (ii) An isotonic solution has the same water potential as the cytoplasm and so no osmosis will occur and the cell will not burst.

Candidate B

(a) (ii) If the tissue is placed in an isotonic solution, both have the same water potential and therefore the mitochondria won't burst, because water isn't entering by osmosis.

e Both candidates have answered the question by describing what might happen if you use distilled water, rather than if you use an isotonic buffer — which is what the question asks. While this is acceptable, it is usually easier to answer the question in the way it is set. Candidate A clearly understands the principles but scores no marks, whereas Candidate B's answer scores full marks. This is simply carelessness by Candidate A as he or she has not identified the direction of osmosis (water **entering** the mitochondria) which is potentially dangerous. Also, Candidate A refers to **the cell** not bursting rather than the **mitochondria**. **Make sure that your answer describes the *subject* of the question. In this case mitochondria are the subject so writing about cells is bound to cost you marks.**

Candidate A

(b) You would prepare the filtrate as in the question and spin the centrifuge at a specified speed that would let you get the chloroplasts. To check it was the chloroplasts I would use a Geiger Muller tube to detect radiation.

Candidate B

(b) Homogenise the cells and centrifuge the mixture at different speeds, drawing off the supernatant at each speed. Most radiation can then be detected using a Geiger Muller tube in the fraction when chloroplasts are obtained.

e Both candidates clearly understand the principle of checking for radioactivity in the chloroplasts to show that they have used the radioactive carbon. However, neither thought to check other organelles to eliminate them and neither was really clear about separating the different organelles after each centrifugation, so both candidates score only 2 out of the 3 marks available.

e **Parts (a)(i) and (b) of this question depend on a basic understanding of cell fractionation, which these candidates clearly have. Part (a)(ii) is based on osmosis which is often a problem area for grade C candidates. Make sure you are able to describe osmosis in terms of water potential and always describe precisely the direction of water movement.**

Question 3

Tissues, organs and the circulatory system

Figure 1 shows part of a capillary network.

Figure 1

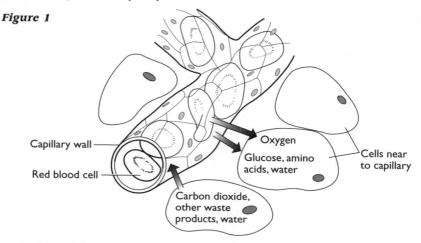

Capillary wall

Red blood cell

Oxygen

Glucose, amino acids, water

Cells near to capillary

Carbon dioxide, other waste products, water

(a) (i) Use the diagram to explain why electron micrographs of capillaries rarely show red blood cells as being disc shaped. (3 marks)

   (ii) Explain why a capillary cannot be considered to be an organ whilst an artery can. (2 marks)

(b) The cells near to the capillaries are surrounded by a liquid called tissue fluid.

   (i) What is tissue fluid? (2 marks)

   (ii) How is tissue fluid formed? (2 marks)

Total: 9 marks

■ ■ ■

Candidates' answers to Question 3

Candidate A

(a) (i) Because the red blood cells are actually larger than the capillary lumen and so they become squashed.

Candidate B

(a) (i) When the sections are cut, it could be from top to bottom or from side to side. The different sections would give different shapes.

   e Neither candidate has got all the three ideas needed for the 3 marks. Candidate A gets 1 mark. Candidate B gets 2 marks for appreciating that the red blood cells are sectioned in an electron micrograph, and that different sections could be at different angles. To get the third mark, Candidate B should have pointed out that the red blood cells' shapes would be distorted because of the small size of the capillary lumen.

Candidate A

(a) (ii) Because an artery actively pumps blood around the body by the muscle in it whereas a capillary just lets blood flow through it.

Candidate B

(a) (ii) Capillaries are only one cell thick whereas an organ is made of several tissues which an artery is; they have specific functions.

e Candidate A has tried to explain his or her answer in terms of function. He/she has hinted at the idea of different tissues by mentioning muscle, but more detail is needed, and no marks are awarded. Candidate B has tried to answer the question appropriately by referring to different tissues carrying out specific functions, but has not related this to an artery by stating what the different tissues in an artery are, and so is awarded only 1 mark.

Candidate A

(b) (i) Tissue fluid is a watery fluid which resembles blood plasma minus its proteins.

Candidate B

(b) (i) Tissue fluid is the liquid which surrounds the cells. It is similar to blood plasma but does not contain blood cells or large protein molecules.

e Both candidates score 1 mark for explaining the chemical nature of tissue fluid, but only Candidate B is awarded the second mark for going on to say what tissue fluid is in terms of function. **When you are asked 'What is …?', try to think of as many 'angles' to your answer as possible.**

Candidate A

(b) (ii) It is formed when blood passes through the capillaries. The capillary walls are permeable to small molecules and ions but not to the red blood cells, platelets and plasma proteins.

Candidate B

(b) (ii) It is formed from blood plasma. At the arterial end of a capillary, the hydrostatic pressure of the blood forces water, small molecules and ions out of the capillary through the permeable endothelial cells. This produces tissue fluid.

e Both candidates clearly understand what will pass out of the blood and why, but only Candidate B is awarded both marks for explaining the driving force behind the filtration process. **When you are asked 'How does…?', you must give full details of the mechanisms involved.**

e This question would not be considered especially demanding by examiners who would expect a grade A candidate to score full marks or nearly full marks and a grade C candidate to score about two thirds of the marks. Much of the question depends on being able to recall specific facts or ideas and you must be prepared to do this. If you cannot answer questions like this, then you are not really prepared for the examination.

Question 4

Molecules in biological systems (I)

(a) Four solutions were made up; one containing glucose, one containing starch, one containing amylase (a starch digesting enzyme) and one containing sucrose. Unfortunately, they were not labelled, except as solutions A, B, C and D. The following tests were carried out to identify the solutions.

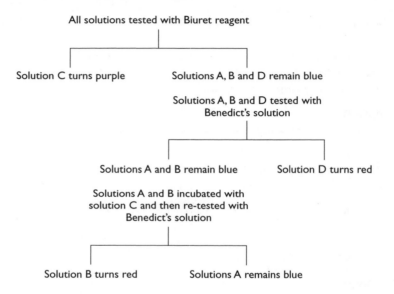

All solutions tested with Biuret reagent

Solution C turns purple   Solutions A, B and D remain blue

Solutions A, B and D tested with
Benedict's solution

Solutions A and B remain blue   Solution D turns red

Solutions A and B incubated with
solution C and then re-tested with
Benedict's solution

Solution B turns red   Solutions A remains blue

Identify, with reasons, the four solutions.   (4 marks)

(b) (i) What is a saturated triglyceride?   (2 marks)

    (ii) Describe one way in which a phospholipid differs from a triglyceride.   (1 mark)

Total: 7 marks

■ ■ ■

Candidates' answers to Question 4

Candidate A

(a) A — starch — identifiable by reaction with iodine/potassium iodide

    B — sucrose — is a non-reducing sugar

    C — amylase — is a protein

    D — glucose — is a reducing sugar

Candidate B

(a) C — amylase — positive result for protein test and enzymes are proteins

    D — glucose — positive result for a reducing sugar and glucose is a reducing sugar

    B — starch — when incubated with C it is broken down into a reducing sugar and C is amylase which only acts on starch

A — must be sucrose — not a reducing sugar and not acted on by amylase

e Candidate A has identified the two chemicals that give initial positive results, scoring 2 marks, but was unable to appreciate the importance of incubating different carbohydrates with amylase. Amylase only acts on starch and the substance that is changed by this incubation must be starch. Candidate A has also involved iodine/potassium iodide, which is not mentioned in the question. **In questions of this nature, do not go beyond the evidence supplied.** Candidate B, however, has identified all four solutions correctly and has supplied logical reasoning to back up the identification, so is awarded all 4 marks.

Candidate A

(b) (i) The fatty acids contained in this triglyceride contain no double bonds and tend to be solid around 20°C and so is a fat and is mainly found in animals.

Candidate B

(b) (i) Triglycerides contain glycerol and three fatty acids. Saturated triglycerides are triglycerides where all the C–C bonds in the fatty acids present are single bonds and it is fully hydrogenated.

e Once again, Candidate B has addressed the subject of the question (saturated triglycerides) fully and has explained both terms — saturated and triglyceride, so gains both marks. Candidate A scores 1 mark for showing clear understanding of the concept of saturated fatty acids. He/she probably knew that there were three of them in a triglyceride but may have thought it was too obvious to mention. **Always address the subject of the question and always state the obvious — the examiner will not assume you know something just because it is easy.**

Candidate A

(b) (ii) A phospholipid contains a phosphate group whereas a triglyceride doesn't.

Candidate B

(b) (ii) Phospholipids have two fatty acids whereas triglycerides have three fatty acids.

e Both candidates have given correct biology in their answers and are awarded the mark. However, neither answer is really complete. Combining the two answers gives a better picture of the difference between the two types of lipid. **Try to make sure that you have supplied enough detail in your answer.**

e Questions such as this, which require you to use keys for identification, can be set on a number of areas. It is usually easy to obtain some of the marks, but others require you to think carefully about the situation. Part (b) ought to be accessible to everyone who has prepared thoroughly and knows their biology.

Blood and the passage of substances

Blood is a complex tissue comprising the plasma and, suspended in the plasma, the blood cells.

(a) Human red blood cells are specialised cells. They are highly adapted to their function of transporting oxygen around the body.

   (i) Explain, in terms of Fick's law, two ways in which the shape of red blood cells makes them efficient at exchanging oxygen with their surroundings. **(3 marks)**

   (ii) How is the absence of a nucleus in red blood cells an adaptation to their function? **(2 marks)**

(b) Figure 1 shows some red blood cells and two different types of white blood cell.

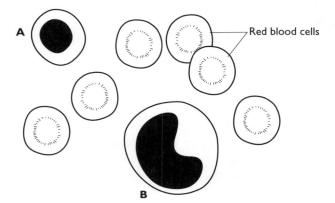

Figure 1

Identify, with reasons, the types of white blood cell labelled **A** and **B**. **(2 marks)**

Total: 7 marks

■ ■ ■

Candidates' answers to Question 5

Candidate A

(a) (i) The surface area of a red blood cell is large because of the biconcave disc. The thickness of the membrane is thin (very) so value is small.

Candidate B

(a) (i) Fick's law states that diffusion rate is proportional to:

$$\frac{\text{surface area} \times \text{concentration difference}}{\text{thickness of exchange surface}}$$

The cells are circular biconcave discs which means that they have a larger surface area-to-volume ratio than a sphere. Because the surface area is greater, according to Fick's law, the diffusion rate will increase. Also they are thin compared to their diameter and therefore the exchange surface is thinner and so the diffusion rate will be quicker.

To gain full marks, a candidate would need to quote Fick's law and describe the thinness of the red blood cell and its large surface area. Candidate B has done all this, but has written far more than is necessary. **Try to be concise — get all the details into a few words — it saves time and is usually clearer to the examiner.** Candidate A hasn't thought it necessary to quote Fick's law — despite the wording of the question, and scores only 1 mark. Also he/she seems confused about **what is thin** — it is the thinness of the cell which is crucial. **Try to be unambiguous in your answers — the examiner will not make up your mind for you.**

Candidate A

(a) (ii) More haemoglobin is present, so more oxygen can be carried.

Candidate B

(a) (ii) Red blood cells contain haemoglobin which carries oxygen, and because they have no nucleus, there is more room for haemoglobin and therefore the transport of oxygen is more efficient.

See what I mean about being concise? Both candidates have scored full marks here but Candidate A has this time managed to say all that is necessary in very few words.

Candidate A

(b) Cell A is a lymphocyte because it is the same size as a red blood cell. Cell B is a phagocyte because it is larger than a red blood cell.

Candidate B

(b) A — lymphocyte because it is the same size as a red blood cell.
B — monocyte because it's larger and doesn't seem to have granular cytoplasm.

Both have correctly identified the lymphocyte for 1 mark and Candidate B has also identified the monocyte for the other mark. Candidate A suggests that cell B is a phagocyte — and it might well be — but a phagocyte is not **a** type of white blood cell. **Several** types of white blood cells are phagocytes and engulf (phagocytose) foreign material in the body.

This is a fairly straightforward question for anybody who knows their biology. The responses reveal the attention to detail that is needed, some of which is missing from Candidate A's answers but is supplied by Candidate B.

The nature and action of enzymes

The rate of enzyme action depends on a number of factors, including the concentration of the substrate. Figure 1 shows the rate of reaction of an enzyme at 25°C at different substrate concentrations.

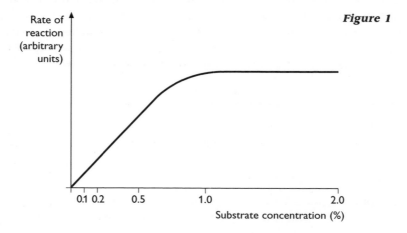

Figure 1

(a) (i) Explain the shape of the graph in terms of kinetic theory and enzyme–substrate complex formation:

A — from substrate concentration of 0.1% to 0.5%

B — from substrate concentration of 1.0% to 2.0% (4 marks)

(ii) Sketch, on the graph, the curve you would expect if the experiment had been carried out at 35°C rather than 25°C. (1 mark)

(b) Figure 2 represents an energy level diagram of a reaction proceeding without an enzyme, and the same reaction with an enzyme.

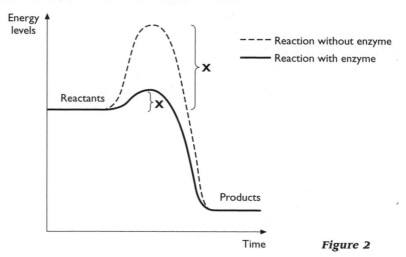

Figure 2

(i) **Describe two ways in which the energetics of the two reactions are similar.** (1 mark)

(ii) **Explain the differences between the regions marked X on the diagram.** (1 mark)

Total: 7 marks

■ ■ ■

Candidates' answers to Question 6

Candidate A

(a) (i) A — the rate of reaction slowly increases from 0.1% to 0.5% because as the substrate concentration increases there are more collisions with the enzyme.

B — the rate of reaction has reached a maximum between 1.0% to 2.0%.

Candidate B

(a) (i) A — as the substrate concentration increases there are more active sites available and so at any one time more binding takes place and the reaction rate increases.

B — V-max has occurred because all the active sites available are used at any one time and saturation occurs so the rate of reaction cannot increase any further and stays constant.

📝 Candidate A explains clearly how an increase in substrate concentration brings about an increase in the rate of reaction from 0.1% to 0.5%. Candidate B tries to supply more detail, but gets confused and seems to imply that the active sites are part of the substrate molecules, rather than part of the enzyme molecules. Candidate A does not explain adequately the shape of the graph between 1.0% and 2.0%. The key feature of the graph here is that it is a horizontal line — meaning no change in rate of reaction. It is not enough to say that it hits a maximum somewhere in that region. Candidate B explains the shape of the graph and the reason why. Read the question carefully — if you are asked to explain the shape of a graph then **explain the shape of the graph** — say what the various changes in the curve mean. Say whether they mean an increase or decrease in rate or no reaction, constant rate of reaction etc.

Candidate A

(a) (ii)

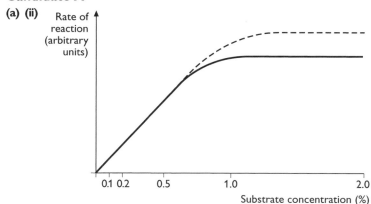

question

Candidate B

(a) (ii)

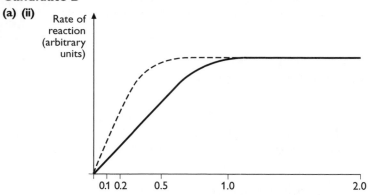

Rate of reaction (arbitrary units)

0.1 0.2   0.5   1.0   2.0

Substrate concentration (%)

e Candidate B shows that increasing temperature will increase rate of reaction at low substrate concentrations so that the enzyme will reach its maximum turnover rate at a lower concentration. Candidate A did not appreciate the importance of the horizontal line between 1.0% and 2.0%. This means that no further increase in reaction rate is possible and must therefore represent the maximum turnover rate of the enzyme. So, it can never react faster than this.

Candidate A

(b) (i) Energy was released from both reactions. Same reactants in both reactions.

Candidate B

(b) (i) Both the reactants and the products are at the same energy levels in each reaction.

e Candidate B has clearly identified two features of the energy level diagram which are the same in the two reactions. So has Candidate A, but only **one** of them is concerned with energetics and so, as there is only 1 mark for the two ideas, the candidate scores no marks here. **Read the question carefully and make sure your answer relates precisely to what the examiner has asked.**

Candidate A

(b) (ii) With an enzyme, **X** is smaller than without an enzyme. Enzymes lower activation energy.

Candidate B

(b) (ii) The activation energy with the enzyme is less than the activation energy without the enzyme.

e Both candidates clearly understand what is a basic concept in enzyme kinetics, so both are awarded the mark here. You must be able to recognise this feature in an energy level diagram of a reaction. Sometimes you may be asked to explain the differences in activation energy as well.

e Enzyme kinetics is quite a difficult area for many candidates. **Of course, you need to know the factors that can affect the rate of reaction and how each affects the rate of reaction, but there are some general principles which can help you to sort out what is happening. Many questions involving enzyme kinetics include a graph, showing how rate of reaction changes with a particular factor, so bear these ideas in mind. If the reaction increases as the factor increases, then that factor is limiting the rate of the reaction and you can explain the increase solely in terms of how that factor affects the enzyme. If increasing the factor produces no increase in the rate of reaction, then there are two possibilities:**

- **the maximum turnover rate has been reached**
- **some other factor is now limiting the rate of reaction**

Microscopy and cell structure

Figure 1 is drawn from an electron micrograph of a cell from the pancreas. The zymogen granules contain inactive enzymes.

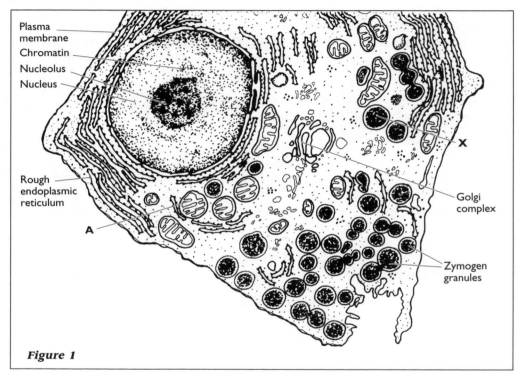

Figure 1

(a) **Name the structures labelled A.** (1 mark)

(b) **Give two pieces of evidence from the diagram which suggest that the cell is synthesising large amounts of protein. Explain your answers.** (4 marks)

(c) **Measure the diameter of the zymogen granule marked X in millimetres. The actual diameter of this zymogen granule is 1 μm. Calculate the magnification of this electron micrograph.** (2 marks)

(d) **Explain why the internal membranes of a cell cannot be seen using a light microscope.** (1 mark)

Total: 8 marks

■ ■ ■

Candidates' answers to Question 7

Candidate A

(a) Mitochondria

Candidate B

(a) Mitochondria

> *e* Both candidates could recognise the mitochondria for 1 mark — and you must be able to as well. There are no other organelles with internal membranes quite like mitochondria!

Candidate A

(b) There are a lot of ribosomes present in the cell which make proteins. The nucleus has many light patches which indicate that it is coding for much mRNA.

Candidate B

(b) There is a lot of rough endoplasmic reticulum present and this is concerned with the synthesis of proteins. Secondly, the large amount of zymogen granules containing inactive enzymes suggests that the enzymes, which are proteins, have been made in the cell.

> *e* Candidate A clearly knows about proteins synthesis but has not really answered the question set. The question asks for **evidence from the diagram** and there are no ribosomes labelled. These would be present on the rough endoplasmic reticulum, however, and do synthesise proteins, so 1 mark is awarded. Also, there is no indication at all that mRNA is being made. Candidate B, however, has given two pieces of evidence which are clearly shown in the diagram and has related these to protein synthesis to gain 4 marks. **Do not go beyond the evidence provided.**

Candidate A

(c) Diameter   = 0.7 mm
                   = 700 µm
Magnification   = 700

Candidate B

(c) Magnification   = measured size
Measured   = 7 mm = 7000 µm
Actual   = 1 µm
Magnification   = 7000/1 = 7000

> *e* Candidate A has measured in centimetres and not millimetres. Neither mark is awarded because the answer is wrong and no method of working is shown. If a correct method had been shown, then 1 mark would have been awarded even though the answer was wrong. Candidate B, however, has given the correct answer with working for 2 marks. **Always show your working in any calculations:** it is easy to get the answer wrong under the stress of an examination but you will usually gain some credit if you show a correct method.

Candidate A

(d) A light microscope cannot magnify as highly as an electron microscope and so small objects like membranes cannot be seen clearly.

question

Candidate B

(d) A light microscope has a low resolution and cannot distinguish between internal and external membranes of a cell.

e You must repeat ten times each night before going to bed that electron microscopes reveal more detail because they have a higher **resolving** power and **not** because of the increased magnification.

e Examiners would expect both grade **A** and grade **C** candidates to score quite well on this type of question. Parts (a), (c) and (d) are fairly common questions and you must be prepared for them. Part (b) demands that you are able to relate the function of organelles to particular processes. Similar questions can be asked about the involvement of a cell in active transport.

Molecules in biological systems (II)

Proteins are made from many amino acids linked into a chain. The chain of amino acids can be split and the mixture of amino acids formed can then be identified using chromatography.

(a) Figure 1 shows a dipeptide.

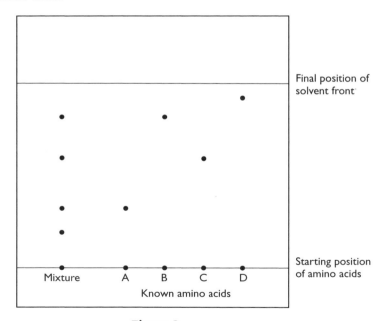

Figure 1

   (i) Underneath Figure 1 show the products which would result from splitting this
        dipeptide.   (2 marks)
   (ii) Name the process which splits dipeptides into amino acids in the body.   (1 mark)
(b) Figure 2 shows a chromatogram produced from a mixture of amino acids and
    four known amino acids.

Figure 2

 (i) From Figure 2, describe the composition of the mixture of amino acids.
      Explain your answer.   (2 marks)
 (ii) Calculate the R_f of amino acid C. Show your working.   (2 marks)

                                                                          Total: 7 marks

8
question

Candidates' answers to Question 8

Candidate A

(a) (i)

$$\begin{array}{ccccc} H & & CH_3 & & O \\ \backslash & & | & & \parallel \\ N & - & C & - & C \\ / & & | & & \backslash \\ H & & H & & OH \end{array} \qquad \begin{array}{ccccc} H & & CH_3 & & O \\ \backslash & & | & & \parallel \\ N & - & C & - & C \\ / & & | & & \backslash \\ H & & H & & OH \end{array}$$

Candidate B

(a) (i)

$$\begin{array}{ccccc} H & & CH_3 & & O \\ \backslash & & | & & \parallel \\ N & - & C & - & C \\ / & & | & & \backslash \\ H & & H & & OH \end{array} \quad \text{and} \quad \begin{array}{ccccc} H & & C_2H_5 & & O \\ \backslash & & | & & \parallel \\ N & - & C & - & C \\ / & & | & & \backslash \\ H & & H & & OH \end{array}$$

> Candidate B has shown correctly the structure of both amino acids which would be formed. Candidate A, however, did not notice the different 'R' groups in the two amino acids. **Look carefully at all aspects of a question.**

Candidate A
(a) (ii) Condensation

Candidate B
(a) (ii) Dipeptide molecules are split in the body into their constituent amino acids by the process of hydrolysis.

> Candidate B has written a whole sentence where one word (hydrolysis) would have been sufficient for the 1 mark. Candidate A has confused the processes of condensation and hydrolysis, so does not score here. **Remember: -lysis means 'splitting'.**

Candidate A
(b) (i) The mixture contains A, B and C. There is a fourth spot which must not be an amino acid because it doesn't correspond with any of the spots.

Candidate B
(b) (i) The mixture of amino acids contains amino acids A, B, C and one other. The fourth amino acid does not correspond with any of the known amino acids.

> Candidate A has correctly identified A, B and C in the mixture, but drops 1 mark for thinking that the fourth spot was not an amino acid just because it wasn't one of the known amino acids. Candidate B gets both marks. The question states quite clearly that the mixture contained amino acids — it makes no mention of anything else. **Read the question carefully and do not make any assumptions which are not warranted.**

Candidate A
(b) (ii) $R_f = 0.8$

Candidate B

(b) (ii) Distance travelled by solvent front = 5 cm.

Amino acid C travels 3 cm.

Therefore R_f is 0.6 (3/5).

e Candidate B has correctly calculated the R_f of amino acid C, with working, for 2 marks. It appears that Candidate A has measured the distance moved by another amino acid. However, if the candidate had shown his or her working, 1 mark could still have been awarded. **Always show your working.**

Plasma membranes

Eukaryotic cells are surrounded by a membrane called the plasma membrane. The structure of this membrane is represented by the fluid mosaic model. Substances which enter or leave such a cell must do so through the plasma membrane. Figure 1 represents the fluid mosaic model membrane structure.

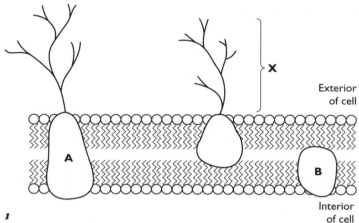

Figure 1

(a) (i) What is the chemical nature of X? Suggest one possible function of this molecule. (2 marks)

(ii) Which protein molecule, A or B, could form an ion channel? Explain your answer. (2 marks)

(iii) Indicate precisely on the diagram one region of this membrane that is hydrophobic. (1 mark)

(b) When red blood cells are placed in distilled water, they swell and burst. Potato cells placed in distilled water swell slightly, but do not burst. Use your knowledge of cell structure and osmosis to explain these observations. (4 marks)

(c) In an investigation into the permeability of membranes, students carried out an investigation using discs of beetroot. Beetroot cells contain a purple-red pigment which, ordinarily, cannot pass through the plasma membrane. The investigation was carried out as follows:

(1) 10 discs of beetroot were cut.

(2) The discs were washed in distilled water until no more colour escaped.

(3) They were placed in 10 cm³ distilled water in a test tube taken from a water bath at 20°C.

(4) The test tube was replaced in the water bath for 10 minutes.

(5) After 10 minutes, the coloration of the liquid in the test tube was measured using a colorimeter.

This procedure was repeated at other temperatures. The results of the investigation are summarised in Figure 2.

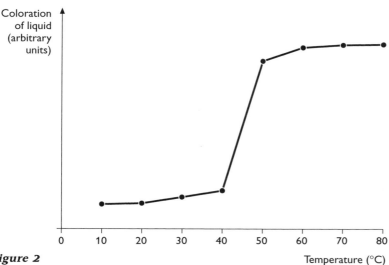

Figure 2

(i) **What causes the coloration in the water in the test tubes?** (2 marks)

(ii) **Describe the change in coloration between:**
   A: 20°C and 40°C
   B: 40°C and 50°C (1 mark)

(iii)**Use the fluid mosaic model of membrane structure to explain the changes**
   described in (ii). (3 marks)

Total: 15 marks

■ ■ ■

Candidates' answers to Question 9

Candidate A
(a) (i) Branched carbohydrate — acts as a receptor for hormones.

Candidate B
(a) (i) **X** is a carbohydrate and is used for cell recognition.

   ℓ Both candidates have correctly identified **X** as a carbohydrate for 1 mark, but only
   Candidate B has understood its function for the second mark.

Candidate A
(a) (ii) **A** because the protein goes past the second layer of phospholipids.

Candidate B
(a) (ii) **A** because it is an intrinsic protein (it goes right through the membrane). It can
   provide a hydrophilic pore through the centre of the molecule.

   ℓ Both identify the correct protein for 1 mark, but only Candidate B explains clearly
   why this protein is chosen.

question 9

Candidate A
(a) (iii)

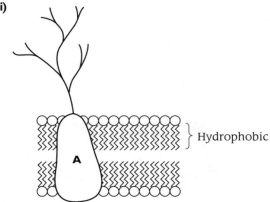

Candidate B
(a) (iii)

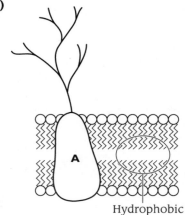

> *e* Both candidates are credited with the mark, although Candidate B's is the better representation. The circle specifically excludes the hydrophilic heads of the phospholipids and also the protein molecules. The bracket used by Candidate A could be taken to include part of the protein molecule.

Candidate A
(b) In both types of cells osmosis occurs. This means that water has entered both cells. This happens because the water outside the cell has a higher water potential than the solution inside. The potato cells do not burst, however, because they are typical plant cells and have a cell wall to prevent them from bursting. Red blood cells are animal cells with no cell wall.

Candidate B
(b) This is because red blood cells are animal cells and potato cells are plant cells and therefore have a cell wall. Both sets of cells swell because osmosis occurs as water moves from a higher water potential outside the cell to a lower water

potential inside the cell. In the red blood cells there is no wall to stop the swelling and so it keeps on taking in water (because distilled water has a water potential of zero) and then it bursts because the membrane is too weak to prevent it.

e Both candidates clearly have a good grasp of what is happening. The only point missed by Candidate A, and 1 mark dropped, is that water keeps entering by osmosis because distilled water has a water potential of zero. Very often, when answering questions on osmosis, you must:
- identify the differences in water potential that exist
- describe the direction of movement of water that will occur as a result (from less negative/higher water potential to more negative/lower water potential)
- explain any consequences that result from this movement of water

Candidate A

(c) (i) The purple-red pigment as it passes out of the cells.

Candidate B

(c) (i) Anthocyanin causes the coloration of the water as it diffuses out of the beetroot cells.

e The examiners would not expect the name of the pigment. This aside, it is clear that Candidate B knew what was happening for maximum marks. So too did Candidate A, but didn't think to mention that the pigment would **diffuse** out. **Always name the process by which molecules are moving if you can — you will often pick up extra marks for doing so.**

Candidate A

(c) (ii) A — there is only a slight coloration of the liquid.
B — there is a big difference in the coloration of the liquid from 40°C to 50°C.

Candidate B

(c) (ii) A — there is a slight increase in the coloration.
B — there is a big increase in the coloration.

e Both candidates have identified the dramatic change that occurs at 40°C. Does Candidate A's answer for A mean there is a slight increase from 20°C to 40°C or does it mean there is the same small amount present? The candidate is given the benefit of the doubt here, as two ideas are needed for 1 mark. Candidate B's answer for A is less ambiguous.

Candidate A

(c) (iii) Between 20°C and 40°C, the phospholipid bi-layer and proteins in the cell membrane are not affected, but after 40°C they begin to vibrate more, causing the membrane structure to become less stable and therefore letting the purple-red pigment escape.

Candidate B

(c) (iii) Between 20°C and 40°C, there is a slight change because as the temperature increases, the molecules in the membrane gain more kinetic energy and so

question

they move around more which increases the gaps in the membrane and so pigment can diffuse through. After 40°C, the increase in temperature starts to denature some of the proteins in the layer which means there will be a rapid increase in the amount of space for anthocyanin to move through.

Candidate A probably didn't identify the small increase that occurred between 20°C and 40°C. Candidate B, however, has clearly explained this small increase and has realised that after 40°C the proteins will be denatured. However, there is no real reference to this altering membrane structure as a whole and so 1 mark is lost.

Most candidates can identify structures in plasma membranes and describe their functions — so make sure that you can. Osmosis is generally understood, in principle at least. Candidates can usually spot when a question is about osmosis. Marks are often lost here because candidates get confused about which way the water will move and, if they get this wrong, they usually cannot explain any of the consequences.

The circulatory system

Read the following passage.

One of the main challenges to maintaining the steady state of the body during heavy exercise is the increased demand by the muscles for oxygen. This may be 15 to 20 times greater than at rest. In order to meet the increased oxygen demand, two major adjustments to blood flow must be made. There must be an increased cardiac output and a redistribution of the blood to the various organs. At the same time, the amount of blood flowing to important organs such as the kidneys and brain must be maintained.

The increased cardiac output is brought about by changes in the heart beat. The redistribution of blood to the various organs is possible because of the structure of the wall of the arterioles. At the same time, breathing becomes faster and deeper to supply the blood with the extra oxygen and remove the extra carbon dioxide which is being generated by the active muscles.

(a) **Explain, as fully as you can, how the cardiac output can be increased.** (4 marks)

(b) **At rest, 15% of the cardiac output passes through the brain. What percentage would you expect to pass through the brain during exercise if the cardiac output increased by a factor of five? Explain your answer.** (3 marks)

(c) **Explain how the structure of the wall of arterioles allows the redistribution of blood to the various organs.** (3 marks)

(d) **The gas exchange system and the circulatory system are sometimes called a 'coupled unit'. Suggest what this means with reference to the response of both systems to increased oxygen demand of the muscles.** (3 marks)

(e) **Suggest why the amount of blood flowing to the kidney must remain constant.** (2 marks)

Total: 15 marks

■ ■ ■

Candidates' answers to Question 10

Candidate A

(a) Cardiac output depends on the heart rate and the stroke volume. If both are increased, then the cardiac output is increased. The stroke volume is the amount of blood pumped each beat and the heart rate is the number of beats per minute, so if either is increased, the cardiac output will be increased.

Candidate B

(a) Cardiac output = stroke volume × heart rate. To increase cardiac output, stroke volume and/or heart rate must be increased. This is done by the medulla in the brain. It is the cardiac accelerator centre of the medulla that stimulates heart rate. When the heart rate is stimulated, stroke volume is increased by the increased return of blood. The hormone adrenaline also increases heart rate.

e Both candidates show that they understand what is meant by cardiac output and what must happen for it to increase. Candidate B, however, goes on to give details of how this is brought about — which is really what the question asks. Candidate A makes no reference to the control of cardiac output by the cardiac centre and so is awarded only 2 marks.

Candidate A

(b) 15%/5 = 3% would pass through the brain if the cardiac output increased by 5×. This is because the amount of blood flowing to the brain must be maintained and at rest it is usually 15%.

Candidate B

(b) 15/100 of blood passes through the brain at rest.
During exercise, cardiac output increases by five but the amount of blood to the brain remains constant, so
15/(100 × 5) of blood goes to the brain.
= 15/500 = 3%

> Both candidates realise that if the cardiac output increases by a factor of five and the blood flow to the brain remains constant, the % flow to the brain must decrease by a factor of five. Also, both candidates have shown their working and so are awarded full marks.

Candidate A

(c) Arterioles have rings of muscle where they join with capillaries. The contraction and relaxation of the sphincter muscles allows the blood supply to the capillary network to be regulated.

Candidate B

(c) Arterioles consist of an endothelium wrapped around by smooth muscle fibres. At the point where they enter the capillaries, arterioles have sphincters. These are circular muscles which prevent blood from flowing into the capillary network when they contract. This allows for the regulation of the quantity of blood which flows through the capillary beds.

> Both candidates appear to understand how arterioles can control blood flow, yet they are not awarded full marks. Why? Largely because neither has really answered the question which was asked. Both realise the importance of smooth muscle in the walls of the arteriole which can contract and relax, for 1 mark, but only Candidate B just about explains the importance of this by saying that when they contract they reduce (prevent) the flow of blood into the capillaries for a second mark. But so what? By contracting, the muscles constrict (make narrower) the arterioles, so less blood can flow into the capillaries and, conversely, relaxing dilates the arterioles and more blood can flow into the capillaries. But Candidate B still hasn't answered the question: to finish it off he or she should have explained that **arterioles leading to some organs are constricted** (so the blood flow is reduced) **while others are dilated** (so the blood flow is increased). That would have explained the **redistribution** of blood.

Candidate A

(d) Both systems are connected because the heart only works faster because the lungs are providing more oxygen at the same time. If more oxygen is available, the lungs will work faster and transport the oxygenated blood faster to the heart. The heart will then have to work faster to pump the oxygenated blood to the organs/muscles which require it.

Candidate B

(d) Both systems are connected and can work together to allow the muscles to get the oxygen they need. The lungs breathe faster to get more oxygen into the body and the heart pumps faster to get the blood round the body faster, allowing the muscles to get the extra oxygen they need.

> Candidate A and Candidate B have both understood the idea of a coupled system, but score only 1 and 2 marks respectively, out of the 3 marks available. The basic ideas examiners are looking for are that the two systems work together to get extra oxygen to the muscles (which both candidates appreciate) and that to do this there must be an increase in pulmonary ventilation to oxygenate more blood and an increase in cardiac output to deliver more oxygenated blood to the muscles. It is these last two specific ideas that are not really addressed by the candidates.

Candidate A

(e) So that the kidneys can continue to filter out urea from the blood.

Candidate B

(e) To allow waste product like urea to be filtered out of the blood all the time as they are poisonous and must not be allowed to build up.

> Candidate A probably understands exactly why the kidneys must continue to filter out urea (because it is toxic) but has just not bothered to write it down, resulting in the loss of 1 mark. **Always look at the mark allocation — 2 marks means examiners are expecting to see two separate ideas.**

> **There are 89 marks available in this selection of questions. The module test will be shorter (although there will still be the two long questions at the end) and contain only 75 marks.**
>
> **Candidate B scored 84 of the 89 marks available. This is not just grade A work — it is the work of an exceptional candidate. You could get a grade A with quite a lot less than this.**
>
> **Candidate A scored 43 of the 89 marks, probably *just* enough for a grade C to be awarded. There are two important points about this candidate's work.**
>
> **(1) The candidate does not perform evenly throughout the test: some questions are answered well, others less well, suggesting gaps in knowledge and understanding. Is this due to insufficient preparation?**

10

question

(2) The candidate could have scored another 9 marks *without knowing any more biology*, just by being careful:

- in question 2(a)(ii), the candidate described osmosis in a *cell*, not an *organelle* (2 marks lost)

- in question 7(c), no working was shown, and the candidate measured in centimetres and not millimetres, so the calculation was wrong (2 marks lost)

- in question 8(a)(i), the candidate did not notice that the two **R** groups in the dipeptide were different (1 mark lost)

- in question 8(b)(i), the candidate did not read the question which specified that only amino acids were present (1 mark lost)

- in question 8(b)(ii), again, no working was shown, and the candidate calculated the R_f of the wrong amino acid (2 marks lost)

- in question 10(c), the candidate clearly understood the way in which arterioles control the distribution of blood, but gave little detail (at least 1 mark lost)

These extra 9 marks could have been scored if the candidate had just been more careful. He/she would then have probably been awarded a grade **B**.

Take care — you cannot afford to throw away a whole grade like this!